PLAYDOUGH

Playing with playdough gives children opportunities to develop useful skills such as hand control, coordination, planning and decision-making. Most young children need little encouragement to start poking, rolling and squeezing the dough. But, as time goes by, the more you can supply in the way of tools and ideas, the more they will learn from it. This book is designed to give you some starting points.

Caterpillar on a leaf

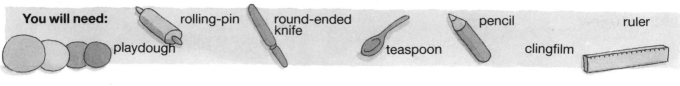

You will need: rolling-pin — round-ended knife — pencil — ruler — playdough — teaspoon — clingfilm

Roll seven or eight balls of different sizes.

Roll out some green dough on clingfilm. Using a knife, cut out a leaf shape and mark veins on it.

Position the balls in a row on the leaf, starting with the biggest and ending with the smallest.

Roll two small balls of dough for eyes. Press them onto the head with the pointed end of a pencil. Make two pencil holes for nostrils and mark in the mouth with the end of a teaspoon.

Other ideas

Ladybird
Flatten a ball of dough, then press the side of a ruler across the centre.

Press on small flattened balls for spots and eyes.

Roll two small antennae.

Attach head.

Poke small white balls into centre of each eye with a pencil point.

Mark mouth with side of spoon.

Mark in nostrils with a pencil point.

Bee
Flatten three balls of dough and press them together. Fix on a round head and a pointed tail.

Press on eyes with a pencil point.

Add two pear-shaped wings.

Mark nostrils and mouth.

See pages 29-32 for playdough recipes and techniques.

Snowman by a pond

You will need: playdough · pencil · teaspoon · tinfoil · twigs · salt · plate · fork

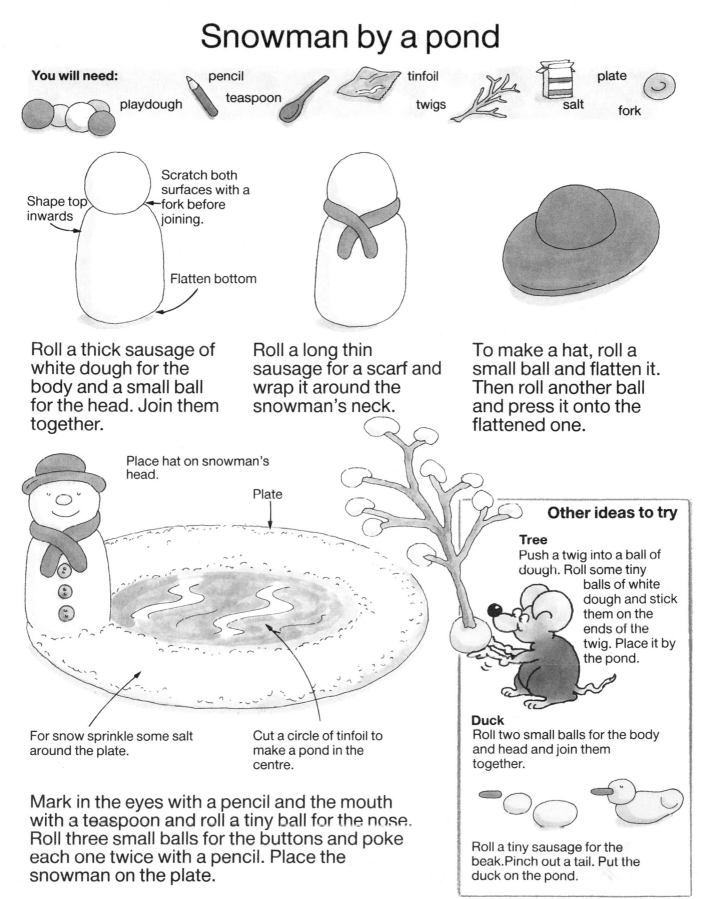

Shape top inwards

Scratch both surfaces with a fork before joining.

Flatten bottom

Roll a thick sausage of white dough for the body and a small ball for the head. Join them together.

Roll a long thin sausage for a scarf and wrap it around the snowman's neck.

To make a hat, roll a small ball and flatten it. Then roll another ball and press it onto the flattened one.

Place hat on snowman's head.

Plate

For snow sprinkle some salt around the plate.

Cut a circle of tinfoil to make a pond in the centre.

Mark in the eyes with a pencil and the mouth with a teaspoon and roll a tiny ball for the nose. Roll three small balls for the buttons and poke each one twice with a pencil. Place the snowman on the plate.

Other ideas to try

Tree
Push a twig into a ball of dough. Roll some tiny balls of white dough and stick them on the ends of the twig. Place it by the pond.

Duck
Roll two small balls for the body and head and join them together.

Roll a tiny sausage for the beak. Pinch out a tail. Put the duck on the pond.

3

Pigs in a pen

You will need: pencil · playdough · box lid or cereal box · small box or cut-down carton · fork · drinking straws

Roll a ball of dough for the body.

Roll four small balls for the feet. Press them on to the body.

Roll a ball for the head. Join the head to the body.

Scratch surfaces with fork to join (see page 32).

Flatten and pinch ears. Press on to head.

Press on snout.

Roll two small balls for the ears and one for the snout.

Roll a thin sausage for the tail.

Mark holes for the eyes and snout with a pencil.

Pig pen and cabbages

You could make several pigs and then make a pen for them.

Cut a doorway in the small box, or cut-down carton. Put it upside down inside the box lid to make a shed.

Cut up some paper or drinking straws for the pigs to lie on.

Make some tiny baby pigs too.

Cabbages

Roll four green balls and flatten three of them for leaves.

Wrap the leaves around the ball.

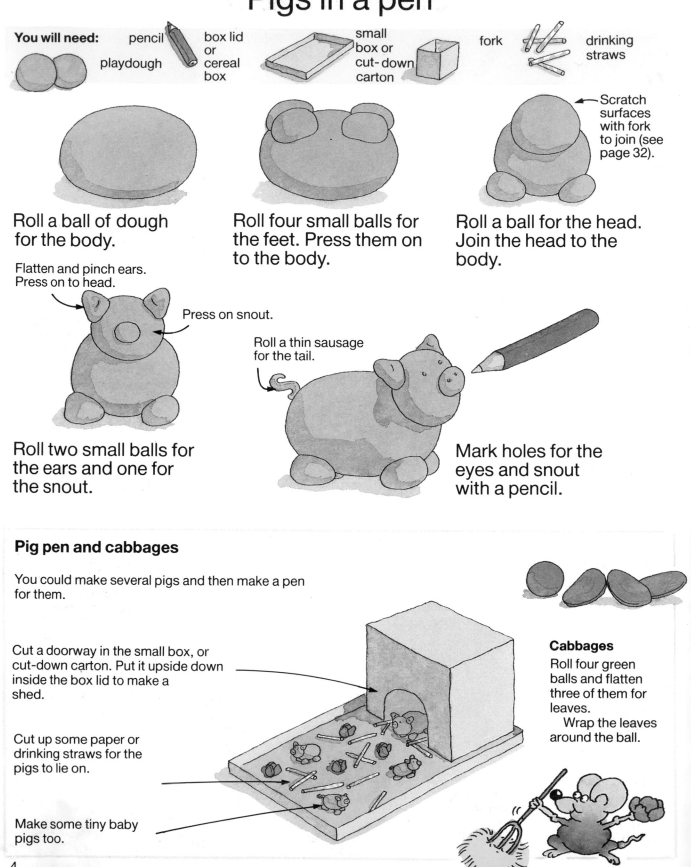

4

Sheep in a field

You will need: playdough, pencil, fork and round-ended knife, box lid or cereal box, sieve or garlic press, paint

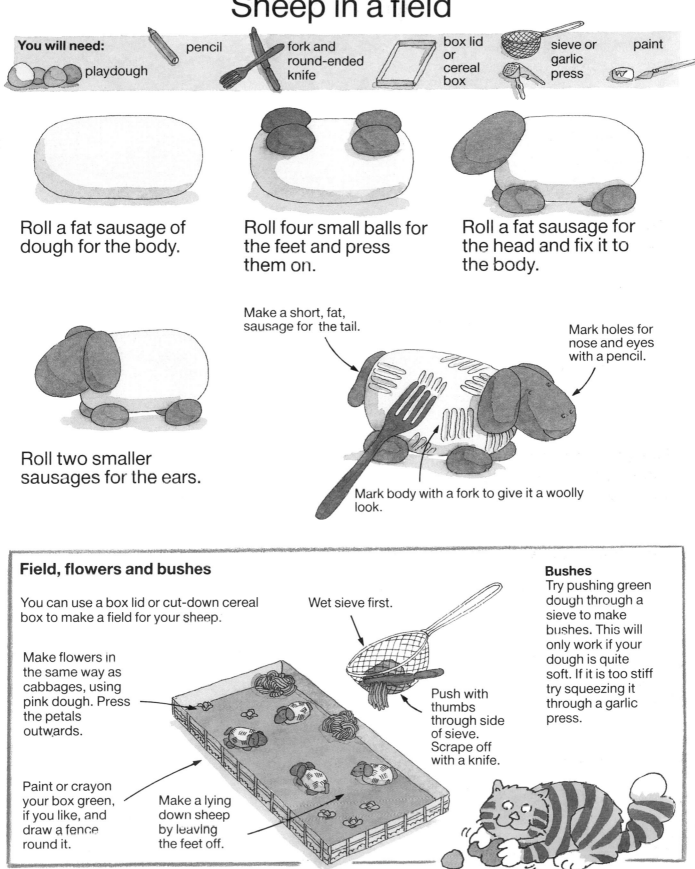

Roll a fat sausage of dough for the body.

Roll four small balls for the feet and press them on.

Roll a fat sausage for the head and fix it to the body.

Roll two smaller sausages for the ears.

Make a short, fat, sausage for the tail.

Mark holes for nose and eyes with a pencil.

Mark body with a fork to give it a woolly look.

Field, flowers and bushes

You can use a box lid or cut-down cereal box to make a field for your sheep.

Make flowers in the same way as cabbages, using pink dough. Press the petals outwards.

Paint or crayon your box green, if you like, and draw a fence round it.

Make a lying down sheep by leaving the feet off.

Wet sieve first.

Push with thumbs through side of sieve. Scrape off with a knife.

Bushes
Try pushing green dough through a sieve to make bushes. This will only work if your dough is quite soft. If it is too stiff try squeezing it through a garlic press.

5

Cat on a cushion

You will need: pencil · rolling-pin · felt-tip pen · straw · saltdough* · lightly oiled baking tray · paint · round-ended knife · clingfilm

Roll a ball of dough for the body. Press in a piece of straw. Attach a smaller ball for the head.

Flatten the bottom.

Roll a thin sausage of dough for the collar and wrap it around the neck.

Roll a thicker sausage for the tail. Press it on and wrap it round. Pinch out the ears.

Mark in the eyes with a pencil point.

Roll a ball of dough and flatten it in the palm of your hand.
    Pinch out the sides to make four corners. Sit the cat on the cushion.

Bake in the oven before painting.*

Mark in the face with felt-tip pen.

Cat on a mat and other ideas

Roll out some dough on clingfilm and cut an oblong shape.

Press patterns in it with a straw and decorate the edges with a knife.

Lay the body of the cat on the mat before adding the head and tail.

A bowl for your cat
Roll a small ball and press the end of a pencil into it.

Fish on a plate
Cut a fish shape from a flat piece of dough. Flatten a ball of dough for the plate.

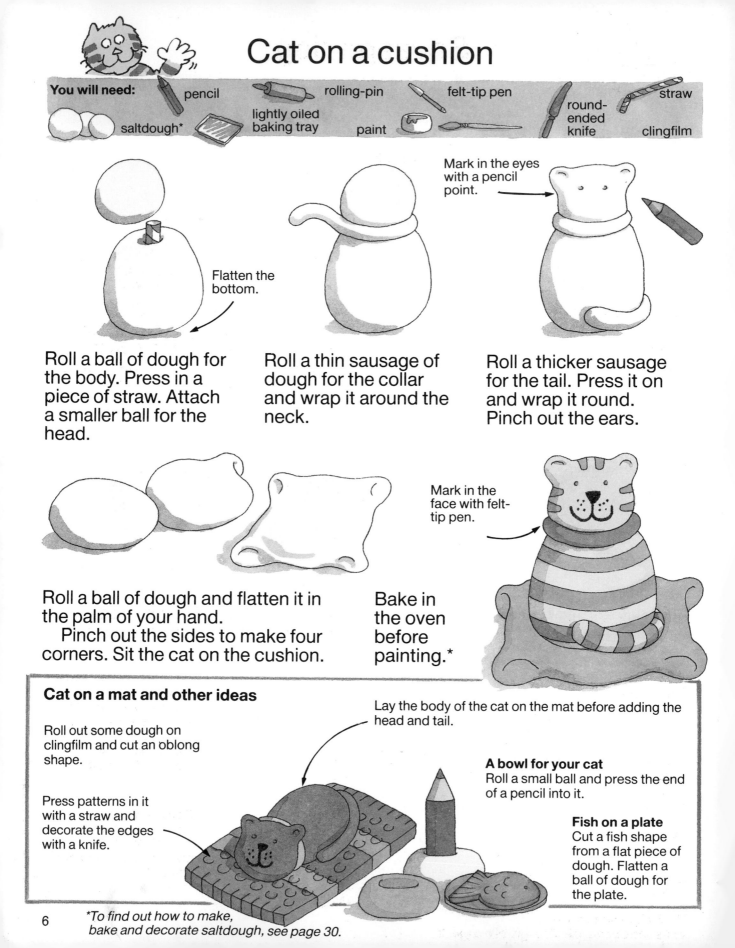

*To find out how to make, bake and decorate saltdough, see page 30.

Sausage dog

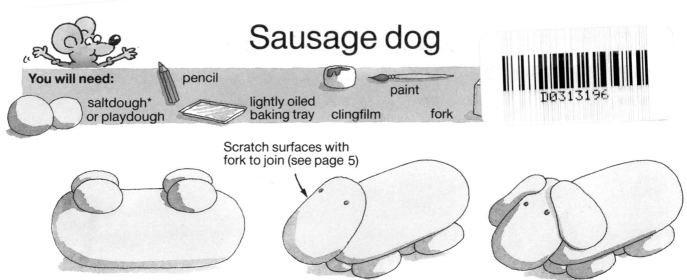

You will need:

saltdough* or playdough
pencil
lightly oiled baking tray
clingfilm
paint
fork

Scratch surfaces with fork to join (see page 5)

Roll a long, fat sausage of dough for the body and press on four small balls for feet.

Roll a short, fat sausage for the head. Join it to the body. Mark in the eyes with a pencil.

Roll two small sausages and flatten them to make ears. Join them to the top of the head.

Roll a small sausage for the tail and a tiny ball of dough for the nose. Press them on.

Mark in the whiskers with a pencil point and the mouth with a teaspoon. Bake your dog and then paint it.

Other ideas

A bowl
Make a bowl for your dog exactly as you make the cat's bowl, opposite. Write the dog's name on it.

A bone
Roll a small sausage and squeeze it in the middle. Make a slit at each end with a knife.

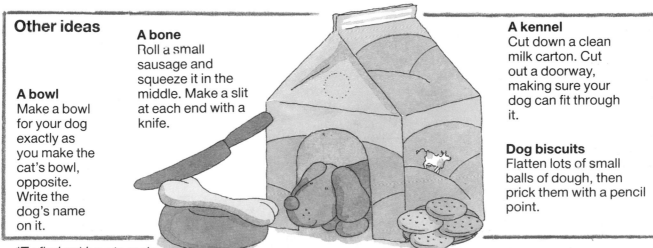

A kennel
Cut down a clean milk carton. Cut out a doorway, making sure your dog can fit through it.

Dog biscuits
Flatten lots of small balls of dough, then prick them with a pencil point.

*To find out how to make, bake and decorate saltdough, see page 30.

Baby in a matchbox

You will need: pencil · rolling-pin · kitchen roll · cotton wool · empty matchbox · paint · clingfilm · saltdough* · felt-tip pen · glue · wool · scissors

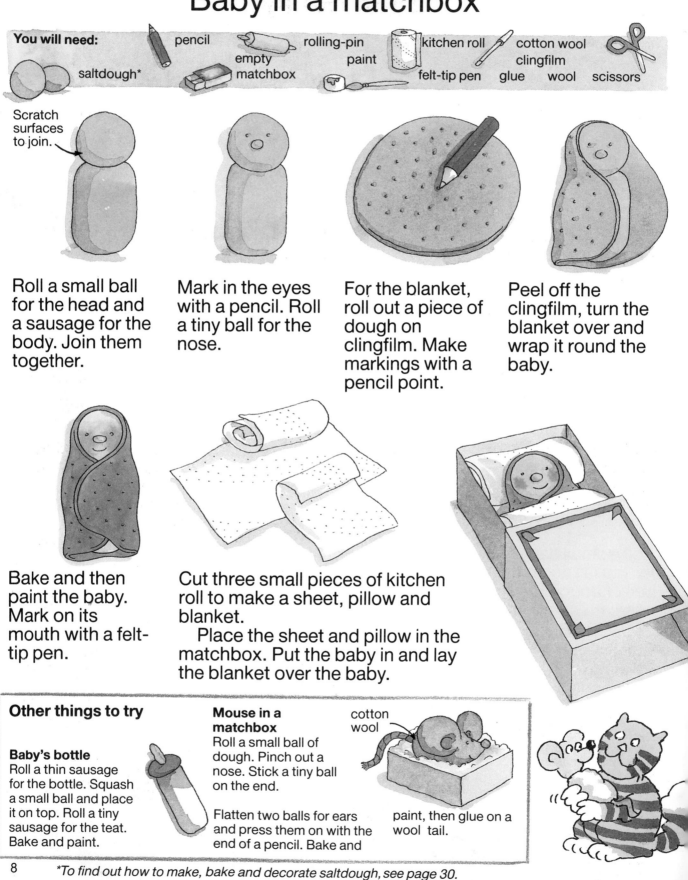

Scratch surfaces to join.

Roll a small ball for the head and a sausage for the body. Join them together.

Mark in the eyes with a pencil. Roll a tiny ball for the nose.

For the blanket, roll out a piece of dough on clingfilm. Make markings with a pencil point.

Peel off the clingfilm, turn the blanket over and wrap it round the baby.

Bake and then paint the baby. Mark on its mouth with a felt-tip pen.

Cut three small pieces of kitchen roll to make a sheet, pillow and blanket.
   Place the sheet and pillow in the matchbox. Put the baby in and lay the blanket over the baby.

Other things to try

Baby's bottle
Roll a thin sausage for the bottle. Squash a small ball and place it on top. Roll a tiny sausage for the teat. Bake and paint.

Mouse in a matchbox
cotton wool

Roll a small ball of dough. Pinch out a nose. Stick a tiny ball on the end.

Flatten two balls for ears and press them on with the end of a pencil. Bake and

paint, then glue on a wool tail.

*To find out how to make, bake and decorate saltdough, see page 30.

Snail family

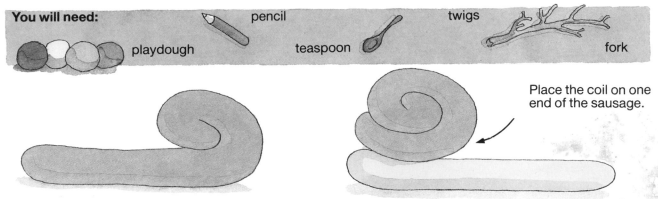
Roll a long, fat sausage of dough into a coil to make the snail's shell.

Place the coil on one end of the sausage.

Roll a shorter sausage and place the coil on top of it.

Bend up the ends and press to the coil. Bend the longer end forward to make a head.

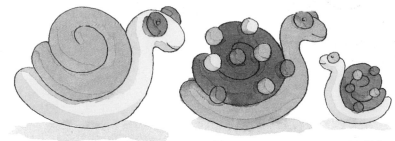

Press on two balls for eyes with a pencil. Mark in the mouth with a teaspoon.

Decorate your snail by pressing little pieces of dough of another colour all over him.
Make a family of snails of various sizes.

Ideas for snakes

To make snakes roll long sausages of dough. Mark in their eyes with a pencil and mouths with a teaspoon.

Snakes in a basket

For the base of the basket, flatten a ball of dough.

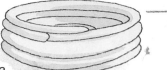

Roll a long thin sausage. Press one end to the edge of the base and coil around.

You may have to make another sausage. Simply press it on where the first one ended and continue coiling.

Arrange some snakes in your basket.

Snake in a tree
Wind your snake around a twig.

These look good on window-ledges.

Hedgehog

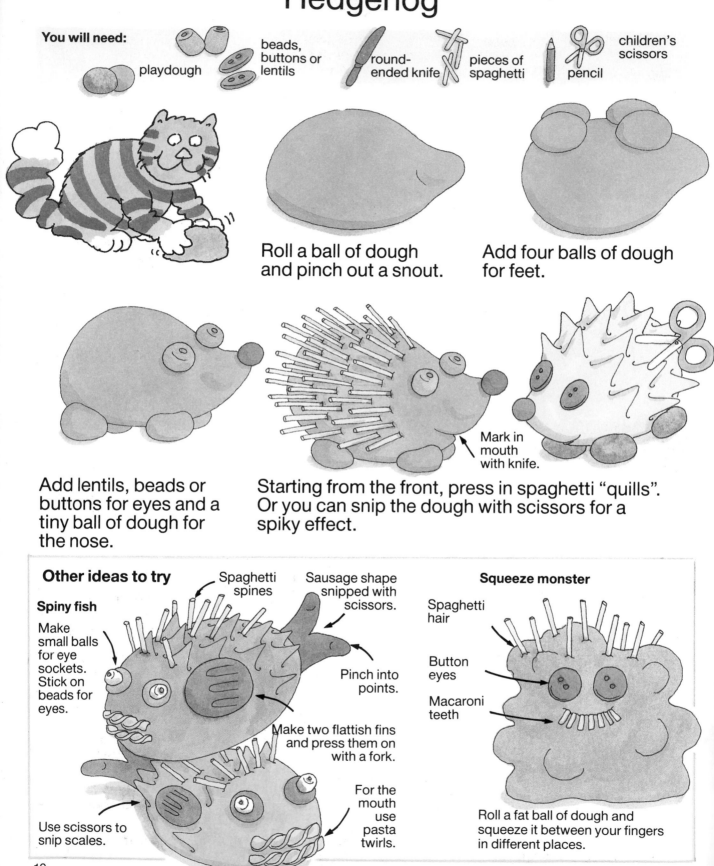

You will need:

playdough

beads, buttons or lentils

round-ended knife

pieces of spaghetti

pencil

children's scissors

Roll a ball of dough and pinch out a snout.

Add four balls of dough for feet.

Add lentils, beads or buttons for eyes and a tiny ball of dough for the nose.

Starting from the front, press in spaghetti "quills". Or you can snip the dough with scissors for a spiky effect.

Mark in mouth with knife.

Other ideas to try

Spiny fish

Make small balls for eye sockets. Stick on beads for eyes.

Spaghetti spines

Sausage shape snipped with scissors.

Pinch into points.

Make two flattish fins and press them on with a fork.

For the mouth use pasta twirls.

Use scissors to snip scales.

Squeeze monster

Spaghetti hair

Button eyes

Macaroni teeth

Roll a fat ball of dough and squeeze it between your fingers in different places.

Dragon

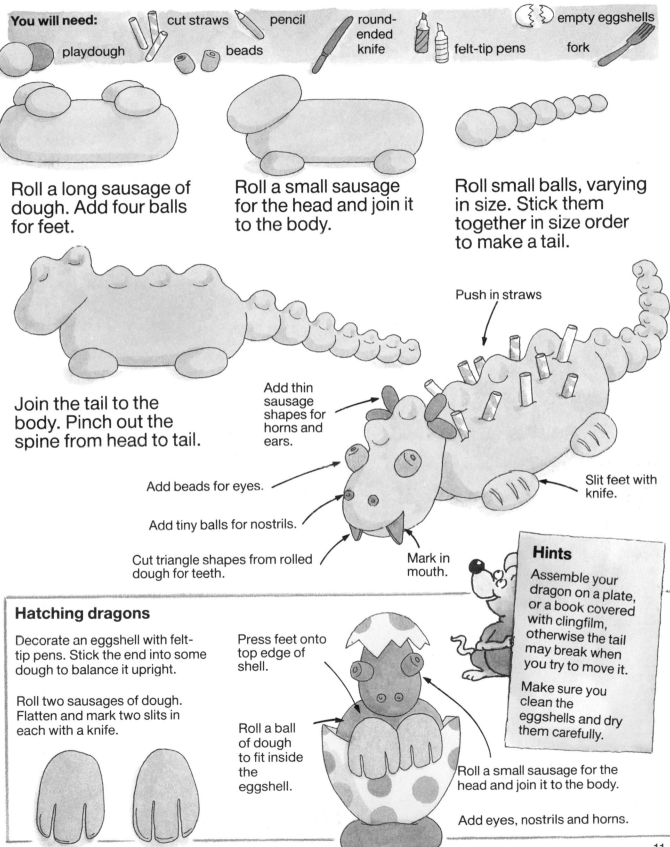

You will need: cut straws, pencil, round-ended knife, empty eggshells, playdough, beads, felt-tip pens, fork

Roll a long sausage of dough. Add four balls for feet.

Roll a small sausage for the head and join it to the body.

Roll small balls, varying in size. Stick them together in size order to make a tail.

Join the tail to the body. Pinch out the spine from head to tail.

Add thin sausage shapes for horns and ears.

Push in straws

Add beads for eyes.

Add tiny balls for nostrils.

Cut triangle shapes from rolled dough for teeth.

Mark in mouth.

Slit feet with knife.

Hints

Assemble your dragon on a plate, or a book covered with clingfilm, otherwise the tail may break when you try to move it.

Make sure you clean the eggshells and dry them carefully.

Hatching dragons

Decorate an eggshell with felt-tip pens. Stick the end into some dough to balance it upright.

Roll two sausages of dough. Flatten and mark two slits in each with a knife.

Press feet onto top edge of shell.

Roll a ball of dough to fit inside the eggshell.

Roll a small sausage for the head and join it to the body.

Add eyes, nostrils and horns.

11

Jewellery

Bead necklace

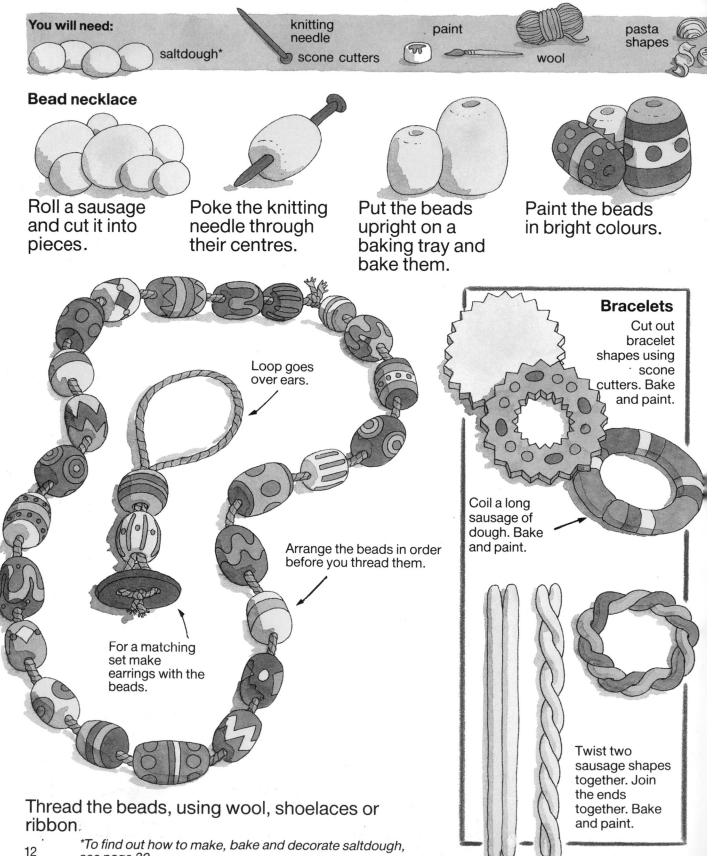

Roll a sausage and cut it into pieces.

Poke the knitting needle through their centres.

Put the beads upright on a baking tray and bake them.

Paint the beads in bright colours.

Loop goes over ears.

Arrange the beads in order before you thread them.

For a matching set make earrings with the beads.

Bracelets

Cut out bracelet shapes using scone cutters. Bake and paint.

Coil a long sausage of dough. Bake and paint.

Twist two sausage shapes together. Join the ends together. Bake and paint.

Thread the beads, using wool, shoelaces or ribbon.

12   *To find out how to make, bake and decorate saltdough, see page 30.

lightly-oiled baking tray

pencil

round-ended knife

shoelaces or ribbon

plaster

safety pin

Teddy earrings

Roll a small ball of dough and flatten for the teddy's head.

Flatten three smaller balls for ears and nose. Join them to the head.

Mark the eyes with a pencil and make a hole at the top.

Bake and paint the earring. Mark in a nose and mouth with felt-tip pens.

Tie a ribbon through the hole.

Hints

Take care to make the holes big enough as the dough will shrink when baked.

For small things like this bake for only 10 to 15 minutes.

Brooches and other earring ideas

Cut-out shapes

Glue on pasta shapes.

Coiled sausages

Put a piece of sticking plaster on the back and stick a safety pin through it.

Make letters out of sausages.

Press in patterns.

13

Playdough people

You will need:

pencil

playdough

round-ended knife

garlic press

teaspoon

pen top

rolling-pin

Man

Mark the back as well.

Add a tiny ball for the nose.

Tiny balls poked in with pencil.

Thin sausage for belt.

Press buckle on with used match end.

Roll a long, thick sausage. Mark his legs by pressing a knife lightly along half his length.

Roll two sausage-shaped arms and small balls for hands. Add two balls for his feet.

Roll a ball for his head. Mark in his eyes with a pencil and his mouth with a teaspoon.

For his hair, cut tiny strips of dough, or press some dough through a garlic press.

Woman

See hint on joining pieces together.

Buttons pressed on with pencil.

Thin sausage for belt.

Decorate skirt with a pen top.

Hints

Secure head to body by pushing in a piece of straw.

Try putting the arms in different positions, or carefully bending the legs, so that your people can sit down.

Roll a thick sausage for her lower body. Add a smaller shape for her chest.

Add her head, arms and feet, as above, and mark in her face.

Give her some hair, then cut a triangle from rolled dough as a scarf.

Other ideas to try

Bags and baskets
For a basket, poke in the centre of a ball of dough with the end of a pencil. For the bag flatten a ball of dough. Make the handles from thin sausages.

Hats
Flatten balls of dough with a finger. Roll small balls and place on top, then squash into shape.

14

Child in bed

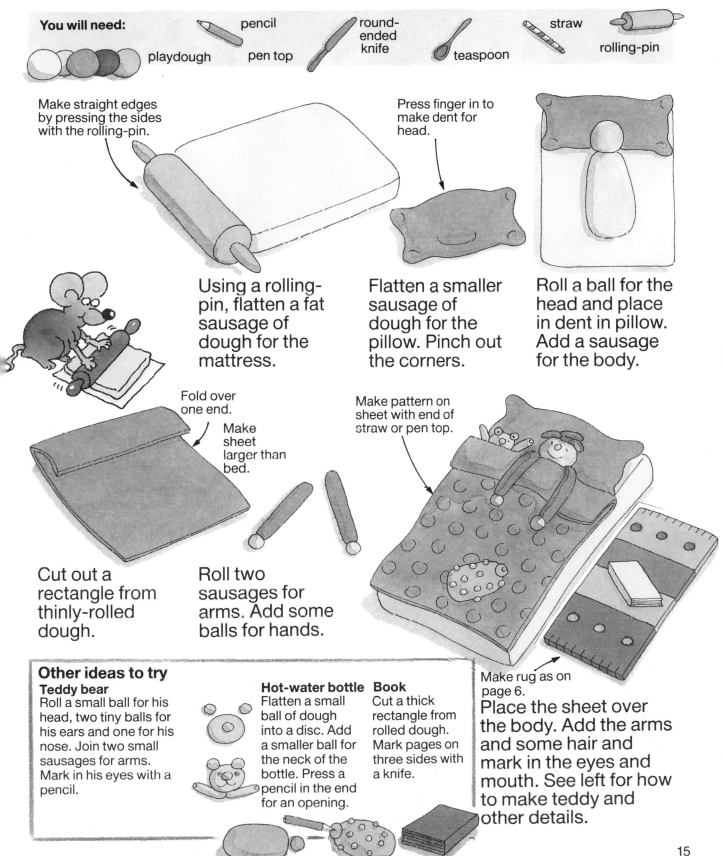

You will need: playdough, pencil, pen top, round-ended knife, teaspoon, straw, rolling-pin

Make straight edges by pressing the sides with the rolling-pin.

Using a rolling-pin, flatten a fat sausage of dough for the mattress.

Press finger in to make dent for head.

Flatten a smaller sausage of dough for the pillow. Pinch out the corners.

Roll a ball for the head and place in dent in pillow. Add a sausage for the body.

Fold over one end.

Make sheet larger than bed.

Cut out a rectangle from thinly-rolled dough.

Roll two sausages for arms. Add some balls for hands.

Make pattern on sheet with end of straw or pen top.

Make rug as on page 6.

Place the sheet over the body. Add the arms and some hair and mark in the eyes and mouth. See left for how to make teddy and other details.

Other ideas to try

Teddy bear
Roll a small ball for his head, two tiny balls for his ears and one for his nose. Join two small sausages for arms. Mark in his eyes with a pencil.

Hot-water bottle
Flatten a small ball of dough into a disc. Add a smaller ball for the neck of the bottle. Press a pencil in the end for an opening.

Book
Cut a thick rectangle from rolled dough. Mark pages on three sides with a knife.

15

Special occasions

You will need: playdough and saltdough* / straw / rolling-pin / teaspoon / pasta shapes / pencil / eggs

A Christmas nativity scene

Mary

Roll a short, fat sausage for her body, so she will look as if she is kneeling.

Add arms, hands and a head. Mark in her mouth and eyes. Flatten a ball of dough for her cloak.

Drape the cloak over her head and body, so it lies in folds behind her.

Joseph and shepherd

Cut down a straw for a stick.

Give them taller bodies. For the shepherd roll a long, thin headband.

For gifts cut cubes from thickly-rolled dough and decorate with pasta shapes.

To make sheep see page 5.

Crib

Roll a fat sausage. Press a bent finger firmly into the centre. Roll four thin sausages for crosses at each end.

Three kings

You can add a feather.

Give them brightly coloured cloaks. Make headbands by joining balls of dough, or twisting sausages.

Make the baby Jesus as shown on page 8. Put him in the crib.

16

round-ended knife

plate

baubles and holly

candle

ribbon

scone cutters

wool

fork

Christmas log candle-holder

Roll a fat, long sausage for the log. Cut each end with a knife and put on a plate.

Roll a small "branch". Cut one end off diagonally, before joining it to the log.

Scratch in a bark pattern with a fork and mark the rings at each end with a teaspoon.

Don't use ribbon, it might catch fire.

Push a candle firmly into the log and then decorate it with baubles and holly.

Saltdough tree shapes

Roll dough out thinly. Cut out shapes with biscuit cutters or a round-ended knife. Poke a hole in each one. Bake and paint*.

*To find out how to make, bake and decorate saltdough, see page 30.

Easter ideas

Egg faces

Roll a ball of dough and stand it on a plate. Press a hard-boiled egg into it, pointed end down. Add hair, faces and hats.

Hen on a nest

Make a hen by pressing together the parts shown above.

Make a disc of dough. Roll lots of thin sausages. Twist them together, then press them round the disc to form the sides.

Roll some coloured eggs to put in the nest.

Hallowe'en party decorations

You will need:

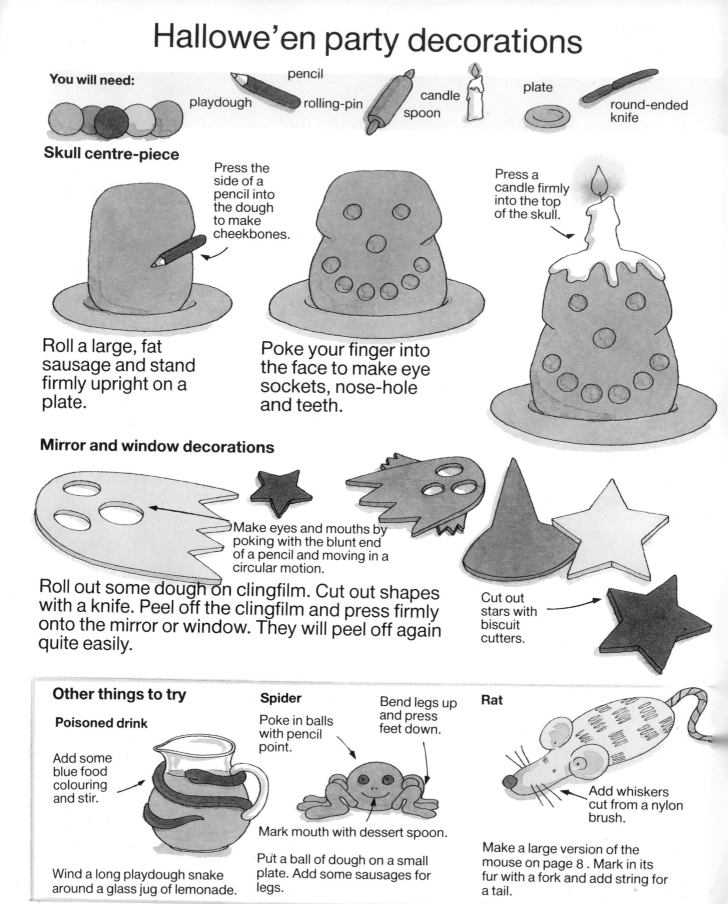

playdough   pencil   rolling-pin   candle spoon   plate   round-ended knife

Skull centre-piece

Press the side of a pencil into the dough to make cheekbones.

Roll a large, fat sausage and stand firmly upright on a plate.

Poke your finger into the face to make eye sockets, nose-hole and teeth.

Press a candle firmly into the top of the skull.

Mirror and window decorations

Make eyes and mouths by poking with the blunt end of a pencil and moving in a circular motion.

Roll out some dough on clingfilm. Cut out shapes with a knife. Peel off the clingfilm and press firmly onto the mirror or window. They will peel off again quite easily.

Cut out stars with biscuit cutters.

Other things to try

Poisoned drink

Add some blue food colouring and stir.

Wind a long playdough snake around a glass jug of lemonade.

Spider

Poke in balls with pencil point.

Bend legs up and press feet down.

Mark mouth with dessert spoon.

Put a ball of dough on a small plate. Add some sausages for legs.

Rat

Add whiskers cut from a nylon brush.

Make a large version of the mouse on page 8 . Mark in its fur with a fork and add string for a tail.

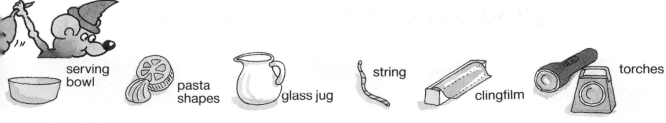

serving bowl pasta shapes glass jug string clingfilm torches

Ghostly hands

Roll two golf ball sized pieces of playdough.

Flatten them onto the outside of a large serving bowl.

Add four sausage-shaped fingers and a shorter thumb.

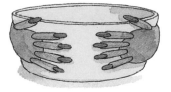

Press some smaller sausages onto the ends of the fingers for nails.

Use the bowl to serve crisps or biscuits.

Add a pasta shell "ring" and mark in the finger joints by pressing with a knife.

Spooky flashlight

Press a ball of dough over the centre of the face of a flashlight. Make a face by pressing in the flat end of a pencil and moving it in a circular motion until a hole appears; mark the eyes, nose and mouth. Shine the light in the dark for a spooky effect. Try flashing it on and off quickly.

19

Dinner on a plate

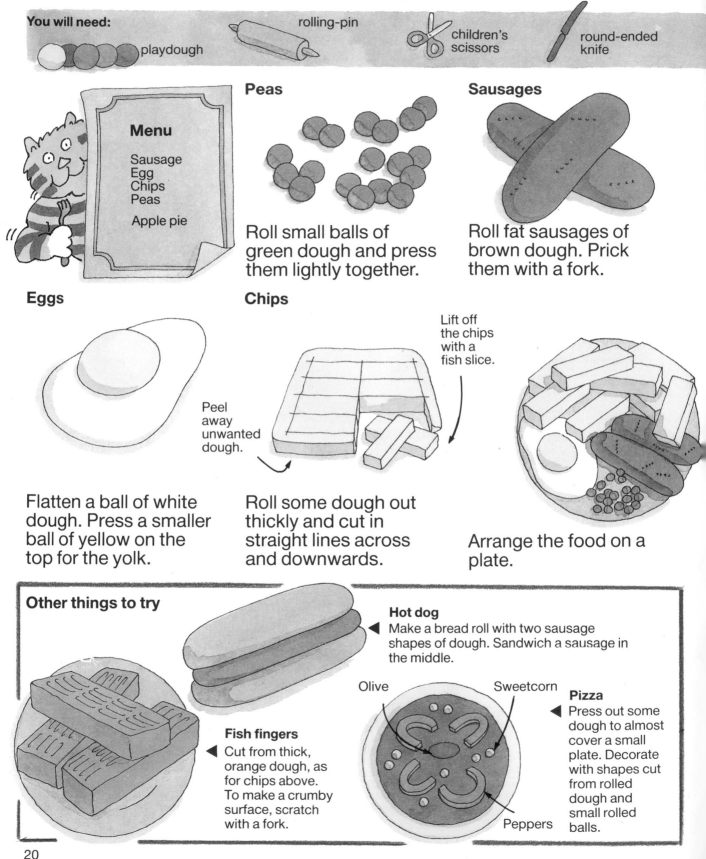

You will need:

playdough · rolling-pin · children's scissors · round-ended knife

Menu

Sausage
Egg
Chips
Peas

Apple pie

Peas

Roll small balls of green dough and press them lightly together.

Sausages

Roll fat sausages of brown dough. Prick them with a fork.

Eggs

Flatten a ball of white dough. Press a smaller ball of yellow on the top for the yolk.

Chips

Peel away unwanted dough.

Lift off the chips with a fish slice.

Roll some dough out thickly and cut in straight lines across and downwards.

Arrange the food on a plate.

Other things to try

Hot dog
Make a bread roll with two sausage shapes of dough. Sandwich a sausage in the middle.

Fish fingers
Cut from thick, orange dough, as for chips above. To make a crumby surface, scratch with a fork.

Olive · Sweetcorn

Pizza
Press out some dough to almost cover a small plate. Decorate with shapes cut from rolled dough and small rolled balls.

Peppers

fork   clingfilm   plates   fish slice

Pastry pie with roses

  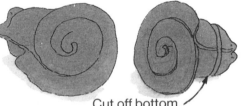

Press out or pat a large ball of dough onto a plate, turned upside-down, for the pie-crust.

Pinch round the edge to make a wavy pattern, or press the knife-blade gently all round the edge to decorate.

Snip some steam-holes in a pattern with some scissors.

Pastry roses

Roll out some dough and cut into long strips, one for each rose.

Roll up the strips. Pinch the pastry together near the base of the roll.

Cut off bottom.

Pull the outside pastry gently outwards to look like wavy petals.

Cut out some leaves. Mark them with a knife and arrange on top of the pie with the roses.

Jellies and other ideas

Press playdough into wetted moulds and gently pull it out. Use small jelly-moulds or bun trays. Roll a red cherry to decorate.

Ice cream

Press balls of dough into a dish. Roll small red balls for cherries. Cut out a wafer with a knife.

Happy birthday cake

Make a big birthday cake, decorate it and add some candles. After the candles and singing cut the cake into slices.

Bread and cakes

Swiss roll

Peel away unwanted dough.

Roll out dough thinly. Cut a rectangular shape.

Lift one short edge gently with a knife. Roll up the dough.

Glaze and bake. Draw in the jam with felt-tip pen.

Fruit cake

Flatten a ball of dough, then poke it with a pencil point. Bake and paint.

Jam tarts

Paint the centres red to look like jam.

Roll small balls of dough. Press the flat end of a pencil into the centre of each. Glaze, then bake them.

Chocolate eclairs

Roll out two long sausages. Press one lightly on top of the other. Bake and paint them.

Hints

Place the items on the baking tray before moulding and glazing.

Remember to remove any plastic from bottle lids before cooking.

Serve on plates made from jam-jar lids, lined with doilies or kitchen roll cut to fit.

*To find out how to make, bake and decorate saltdough, see page 30.

lightly-oiled baking tray

metal bottle-top

doilies or kitchen paper

plates

clingfilm

Cherry buns

Roll small balls of dough.

Add a tiny ball for a cherry.

Flatten small balls between your fingers for icing.

Bake and paint.

French sticks

Make cuts with knife.

Roll a long sausage. Glaze and bake.

Granary loaf

Roll a ball of dough. Glaze, bake and paint.

Cottage loaf

Roll a ball of dough. Add a smaller ball and poke in with a pencil.

Rolls and biscuits

Mark with a pencil.

Roll small balls of dough for rolls. For biscuits flatten them between your fingers.

Pies

Don't fill it right to the top.

Roll a ball of dough and press into a bottle lid.

Decorate it with a small ball of dough. Mark it with a straw. Bake and paint.

Scones

Dip pen top in flour before cutting.

Squeeze to release dough.

Roll out some dough, not too thinly. Cut out some scone shapes with a pen top. Bake.

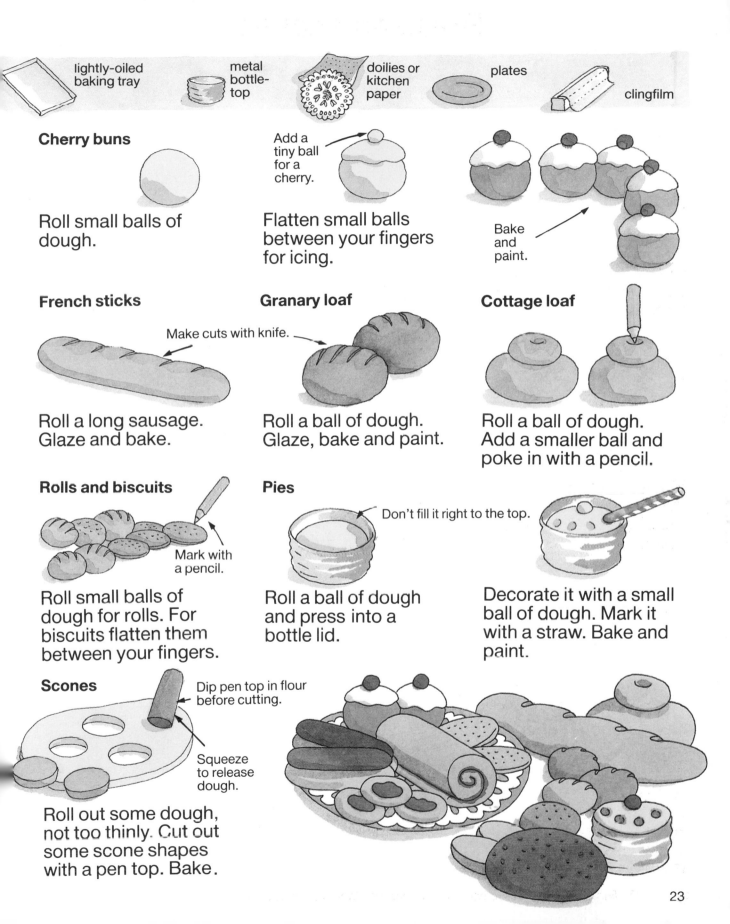

23

Baker's shop

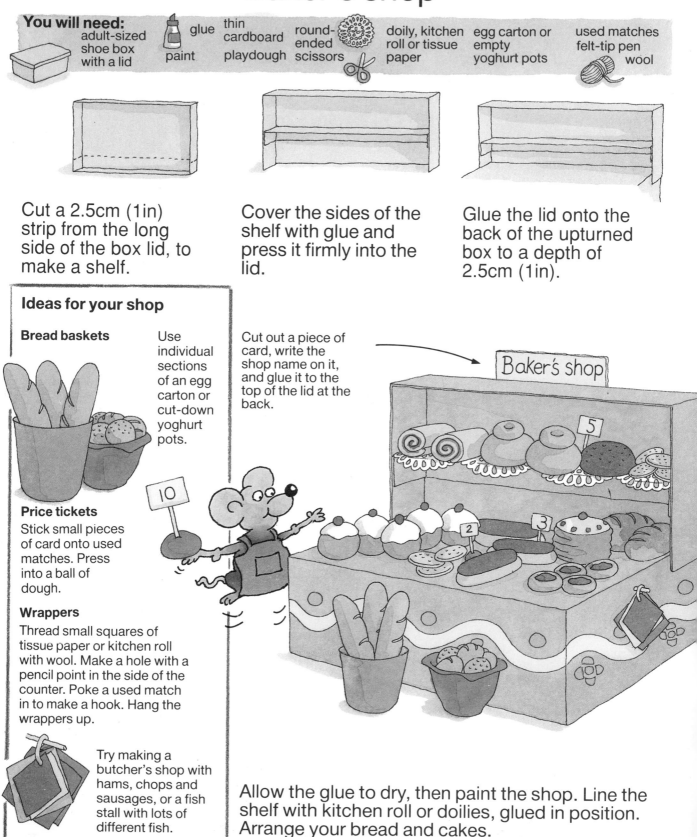

Cut a 2.5cm (1in) strip from the long side of the box lid, to make a shelf.

Cover the sides of the shelf with glue and press it firmly into the lid.

Glue the lid onto the back of the upturned box to a depth of 2.5cm (1in).

Ideas for your shop

Bread baskets

Use individual sections of an egg carton or cut-down yoghurt pots.

Price tickets

Stick small pieces of card onto used matches. Press into a ball of dough.

Wrappers

Thread small squares of tissue paper or kitchen roll with wool. Make a hole with a pencil point in the side of the counter. Poke a used match in to make a hook. Hang the wrappers up.

Try making a butcher's shop with hams, chops and sausages, or a fish stall with lots of different fish.

Cut out a piece of card, write the shop name on it, and glue it to the top of the lid at the back.

Baker's shop

Allow the glue to dry, then paint the shop. Line the shelf with kitchen roll or doilies, glued in position. Arrange your bread and cakes.

Picnic food

You will need: saltdough*   round-ended knife   drinking straw   egg glaze (see page 29)   paints   felt-tip pens   pastry cutters or aerosol can lids   kitchen roll   round-ended scissors

Sausage rolls

You could use a felt-tip pen to colour the filling brown.

Roll small sausages then press a straw into each end to make the filling.

Make cuts across the top with a knife. Glaze them, then bake them.

Cheeses

For holey cheese prick with a pencil point.

Flatten a ball into a disc. Cut wedges. Bake, cool, then paint.

Sandwiches

Roll out dough about 1cm (½in) thick. Cut a square with a knife, then cut into quarters.

Separate the four pieces and bake. Draw a felt-tip line round each piece for the filling.

Ideas for your picnic

Hamper
Use a hinged egg carton. Make holes for wool or ribbon handles by pushing a pencil point through the cardboard.

Plates
Make them from dough, or use jar lids.

Bring some food along from the baker's shop and the vegetable stall.

Beakers
Use toothpaste tube caps or bottle tops.

Tablecloth
Use a square of kitchen paper decorated with dots of felt-tip.

Napkins
Cut small squares of kitchen paper and fold into four. You can make napkin rings by fastening long sausage shapes into a circle, baking and painting.

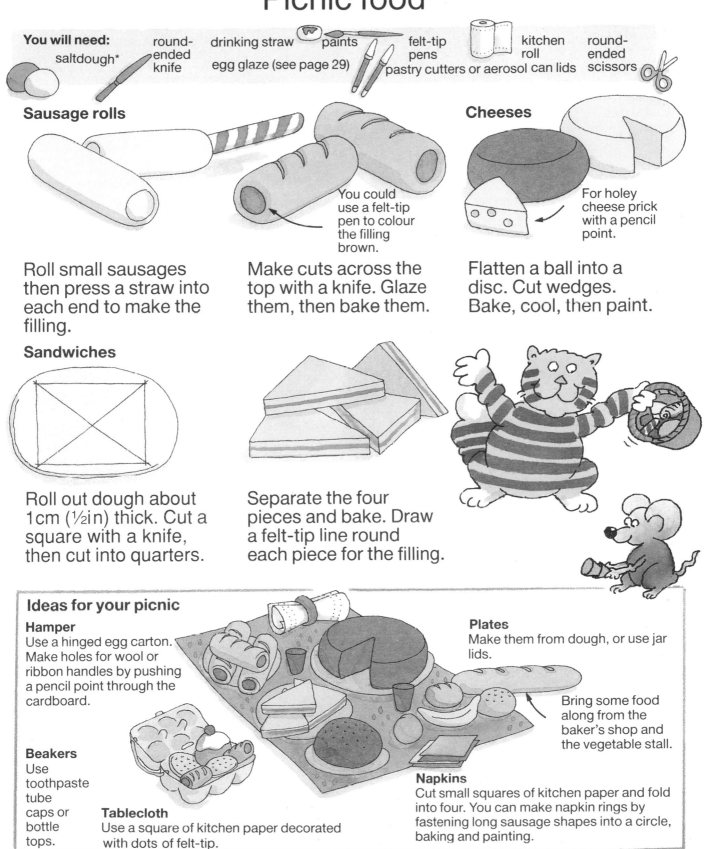

*To find out about making and baking saltdough, see page 30.

Fruit and vegetable stall

You will need: round-ended knife, saltdough*, pencil, lightly-oiled baking tray, cooling tray, sellotape, egg boxes, paint, oven gloves, thin cardboard, felt-tip pens, glue

Potatoes

Roll small balls. Squash into knobbly shapes. Mark eyes with pencil point.

Peppers

Roll short, fat sausages. Make criss cross marks with a knife across the top.

Cucumbers

Roll long sausages, thinner at one end than the other. Make long marks lengthways with a knife.

Marrows

Roll fat sausages. Draw in stripes with felt-tip pens.

Cauliflower

Push three small balls of white dough together. Flatten small green balls of dough to make leaves. Overlap the leaves round the centre. Mark the centre with a pencil point.

Carrots

Roll sausage shapes thinner at one end. Add some green leaves and make marks around the carrots with a knife.

Apples

Roll small balls and poke a pencil point into the tops.

Bananas

Roll sausage shapes and curve them. Draw on felt-tip markings.

Oranges

Roll small balls. Mark peel with pencil point.

Spring onions

Roll very skinny sausages and press them together into bundles. Colour the ends green.

Glue on a sign for the stall.

my stall

Put all your fruit and vegetables into an egg box.

Hint
These items are small and will bake hard in around 20 minutes at gas mark 4, 180°C (350°F).

Use cut-down sections of egg box for additional baskets.

*To find out about making, baking and colouring saltdough, see page 30.

26

Using playdough as a mould

Badge

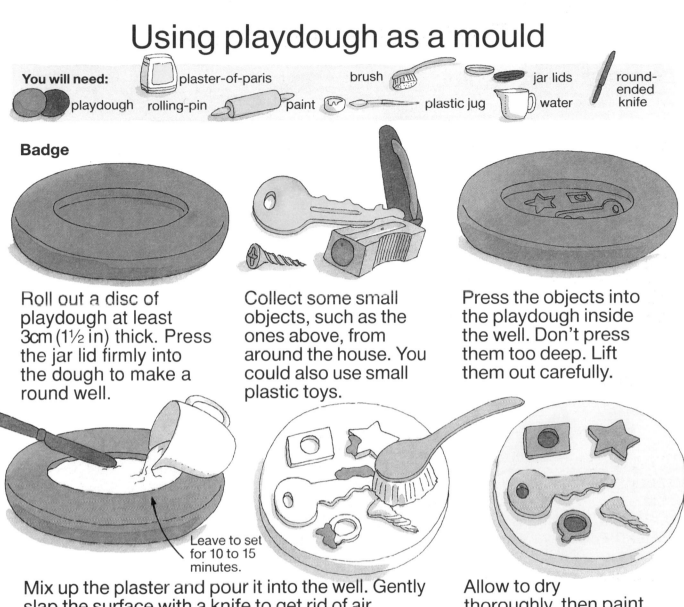

Roll out a disc of playdough at least 3cm (1½ in) thick. Press the jar lid firmly into the dough to make a round well.

Collect some small objects, such as the ones above, from around the house. You could also use small plastic toys.

Press the objects into the playdough inside the well. Don't press them too deep. Lift them out carefully.

Leave to set for 10 to 15 minutes.

Mix up the plaster and pour it into the well. Gently slap the surface with a knife to get rid of air bubbles.

When dry, carefully pull off the playdough. Scrub the plaster clean with a washing up brush, under a tap.

Allow to dry thoroughly, then paint. Fix a safety-pin on the back with sticking plaster (see page 7).

Other things to try
Name plaque
Roll out some dough quite thickly and press a date-box lid upside down into it to make a frame.

Write your name on greaseproof paper and turn it over to use as a pattern.

Press plastic letters into the dough, following the pattern. Pour in plaster. Allow it to set. Scrub and paint.

Hand moulds
Press your foot or outspread hand into a thick piece of rolled-out dough. Lift it out carefully to leave a clear outline. Pour in plaster and leave it to set.

Allow to dry thoroughly, then paint.

Hint

Don't dispose of wet plaster down the sink. Put it in a plastic bag, allow it to set, then put it in the rubbish bin.

Dough shapes you can eat

When you have made the shapes you want, leave them to rise in a warm place for between 30 and 55 mins. Glaze them then bake as specified on packet.

Butterfly

Cut one third lengthways

Roll a long sausage. Snip one end with some scissors

Make wings by flattening balls. Press them onto the body.

Curl the snipped dough round to make antennae.

Tortoise

Mark in the eyes with a pencil point.

Clingfilm

Mark the shell with a knife.

Pat a piece of dough into a dome shape.

Roll out shapes for a head, legs and tail.

Lift up the edges and tuck the feet, head and tail underneath.

Hints

Where pieces of dough need joining, dip a finger in water and wet both surfaces.

Work directly onto the baking tray to avoid spoiling shapes when you move them.

Always handle the dough on a lightly-floured surface.

Octopus

Press on eyes with pencil point.

Mark mouth with teaspoon.

Roll a fat sausage and press it out into an oblong.

Make tentacles by snipping with scissors.

Pull down tentacles and curl around.

Other ideas

Try the snake on page 9, or the hedgehog on page 10.

Letter buns

Using sausage shapes of dough make the letters of your name.

28

Playdough and saltdough

You can buy playdough in toyshops or large newsagents or you can make it yourself. You simply mix the ingredients and heat them on a stove, or in a microwave oven.

If you want to make things that will go hard so you can keep them and play with them, you need to use saltdough.

To make saltdough you combine the ingredients without cooking them. When you have made what you want you can harden it by baking it in the oven.

The things you will need for each project in the book are listed across the top of each page. Sometimes playdough is specified, sometimes saltdough with baking and painting instructions. However, if you want to you can do all the projects with playdough or with saltdough.

How to make playdough

Ingredients:

200g (7oz) plain flour

100g (3½oz) salt

2 tsps cream of tartar

1tbs oil

300ml (12fl.oz) water

A few drops of food colouring

- Put the flour, salt, cream of tartar and oil into a large saucepan.
- Add the food colouring to the water.
- Add the liquid gradually to the ingredients in the saucepan and mix it in thoroughly to get rid of as many lumps as possible.
- Put the pan over a medium-low heat and cook, stirring constantly. This is quite hard work. The mixture will be very liquid at first, then begin to thicken suddenly.
- Continue to stir until the dough becomes very stiff.
- Remove the pan from the heat and scrape out the dough with a wooden spoon onto a smooth surface.
- Put the pan to soak immediately.

Warning: playdough looks very tempting at this stage, but the inside will still be very hot, even when the outside has cooled. Before using, slice it in half with a knife and test it warily with your finger.

- Knead it thoroughly until it becomes smooth and pliable and holds its shape well.

Using a microwave

This method involves much less physical effort and produces excellent results. The instructions given are for a 650 watt oven. Adjust accordingly.

- Mix the ingredients as for pan-cooked playdough (see below left) but use a large bowl suitable for microwave use.
- Put the bowl, uncovered in the microwave.
- Cook at full power for one minute.
- Using oven gloves remove it from the oven and stir well.
- Replace the bowl and continue cooking until the mixture starts to leave the side of the bowl and becomes very stiff – approximately 2-2½ minutes. (Stir at least once during this time.)
- Using oven gloves, remove from the oven onto a heatproof surface.
- Scrape out the dough with a wooden spoon onto a smooth surface.
- Knead as before.

Storing playdough

Playdough needs to be kept in an airtight container to stop it drying out.

Bought playdough should keep indefinitely when stored in its pot with the lid firmly on.

Store homemade playdough in a polythene food bag, inside an airtight box or jar.

If left exposed to the air a salty crust will form on it. You can rescue it by kneading it thoroughly with a little oil.

Colour mixing

You can create most of the colours you might want by mixing blue, scarlet and yellow. If you have pink and green as well it extends your range considerably.

Blue + scarlet = brown

Blue + pink = purple/mauve

Blue + yellow = green

Yellow + scarlet or pink = orange

Scarlet + green = warm shades of brown

Green + yellow = acid green

Green + blue = dark leaf green

Experiment with different combinations. Mix colours on saucers first, before adding them to the water.

Build up a library of colours. Make smaller quantities of those you think you will use least.

The colour will not come out onto your hands during use, but it is advisable to keep it off carpets.

Saltdough

Saltdough recipe

Ingredients:

300g (11oz) plain flour

300g (11oz) salt

1 tbs oil

Approximately 200ml (7fl.oz) water

- Mix all the ingredients in a large bowl using a knife. The dough should feel pliable – add more liquid if necessary.
- Turn out onto a floured surface and knead thoroughly until very smooth and elastic.

Saltdough improves with keeping. Its texture becomes finer and less grainy. It is best made the day before you need it.

Warning

Salt can sting. Protect small cuts and grazes on the hand with sticking-plaster.

Storing saltdough

The uncooked dough keeps indefinitely in a plastic bag in the fridge. If it goes a little soft, knead some flour into it before use.

Colouring saltdough

You can colour saltdough while you are making it by adding food colouring to the mixing water. The colour will go a little lighter when the dough is baked.

   Where small quantities of coloured dough are needed, as for the vegetables on page 26, mix the colours you want on separate saucers, then knead in small portions of white uncooked dough until evenly coloured.

Painting

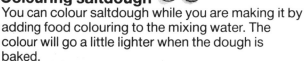

Instead of using food colouring you can paint saltdough after it has been baked. Use powder, poster or watercolour paints.

   You could just add the finishing touches with paint or felt-tip pens.

   Painting will soften the dough temporarily. Allow it to dry out again in the air or still warm oven. Place painted items on a cake cooling rack to dry quickly without spoiling.

Glazing

This gives dough a lovely golden brown colour. Try it for the miniature breads on page 23.

   Simply beat a whole egg and paint onto the uncooked saltdough with a pastry brush or paintbrush.

Baking saltdough

Cook small items for between 10 and 20 minutes, depending on their size, on a lightly-oiled baking tray or roasting tin at gas mark 4, 350F, 180C in the centre of the oven.

Larger items are best cooked overnight at gas mark ½, 250F, 130C. This avoids the dangers of cracking or the dough beginning to brown on the outside while the centre is still uncooked. Precoloured dough may brown very slightly on cooking. The dough is also liable to balloon out of shape if cooked at too high a temperature.

Don't worry if the inside is still a little spongy even after cooking overnight; the salt in the dough acts as a preservative and the centre will air-dry and harden after a while. The larger and thicker the item the longer the drying-out time will be.

You can safely bake small items with larger ones overnight at a low temperature.

Do not use thin trays or cake tins if cooking overnight; they will brown and spoil and scorch coloured dough.

There may be some cracking if your oven is too hot. This is usually underneath the piece and does not spoil the look of the finished article. Experience will tell you how the dough behaves in your own oven.

Saltdough expands slightly on cooking. Keep this in mind while shaping. Make good-sized holes for threading, so they don't close up during baking.

Microwave ovens are not suitable for baking saltdough. The dough tends to balloon out of shape and the salt burns easily.

Always warn of the dangers of a hot oven or baking tray and make a noticeable display of wearing oven gloves.

Tools

Surfaces to work on

Work on smooth surfaces such as formica or polyurethaned wood, or turn trays upside down so that the rim does not get in the way. You can also work on large flat books wrapped in clingfilm.

Playdough rolled out onto a piece of clingfilm lifts and peels off beautifully, leaving a lovely smooth surface on the underside.

When working with saltdough lightly dust the surface with flour.

Tools you may need

 A rolling-pin. You could use a piece of dowelling, or a broom handle instead, or use one from a child's baking set.

 Knives. For safety always use round-ended ones. Plastic knives are safe and light to handle.

 Scissors. For safety use round-ended ones and child-sized ones for easy use. Use for snipping raised patterns (e.g. the hedgehog's quills on page 10), or cutting dough cleanly to mark in mouths and so on.

 Forks. Use for scratching or pressing patterns into the dough, or for scratching two surfaces to be joined. Plastic forks are light and easy to handle, but be careful the prongs are still sharp.

 Spoons. These are very useful for marking curved mouth shapes. Use the side of a dessert-spoon for a large mouth and the tip of a teaspoon for a small one.

 Sieve. A large-meshed metal one is best. These can be used to push dough through so it forms fine strings. Push clumps gently together to make bushes (page 5), or hair for figures or animals. It may help to wet the sieve, shaking off excess water, to enable the dough to be pushed through more easily.

Use the sieve also for washing small objects, like buttons or beads, which are smeary after being pushed into dough. Put them in the sieve, then swish them around in warm soapy water. Rinse them under the tap, then turn them out onto a kitchen roll to dry.

 Pencil. This is very useful for pressing in eyes with the pointed end, making patterns with either end, or pressed sideways into the dough. Alternatively use a child's knitting needle.

 Cutters. Use scone or biscuit cutters, upturned plastic tumblers, or plastic tops from aerosol cans (flour lightly before use, squeeze gently to release dough). Plastic pen tops make tiny cutters (e.g. for miniature scones on page 23).

 Fish slice. This is useful for lifting and transferring pieces without damage, or removing hot saltdough items from baking tray to cooling rack, or pressing patterns into dough.

 Other tools. Straws, used matchsticks, keys, pasta, beads, buttons, shells, pebbles. Anything which will make a clear imprint in dough can be used to build up a pattern.

 Moulds. Small bun trays or jelly moulds can be used. Push dough firmly into the wetted mould. Ease away from the sides and pull out gently to make "cakes" and "jellies". Try using the moulded plastic containers from chocolate or toy-packaging.

Use playdough itself as a mould. Impressions can be made in the dough and a cast taken with plaster (see page 27).

Techniques

Starting off

Once they have learnt how to make some simple, basic shapes children will soon be able to decide how to go about putting their own ideas into practice. The projects in this book are mostly created from varying sizes of ball shapes or sausage shapes.

Rolling balls

Show children how to pinch off a piece of dough and press it into a rough ball shape.
- Place it on the flat palm of an open hand.
- Lay the other hand on top and roll gently between the palms with a circular motion.
- Turn the ball a few times in between rolling until you have a good shape.
- Or place the roughly-shaped ball onto a smooth surface and roll with a circular movement under your open palm.
- To roll several balls of the same size pinch off a piece of dough, divide it into two, then divide each piece in two, and so on until you have the number you want. This way you can make ears, feet and so on that match in size.
- Tiny balls for noses, buttons and so on can be rolled in the palm of your hand with a finger-end. The ball will stick to the end of your finger; lift gently and press in position.

Discs

- These can be made by patting a ball evenly with the palm of your hand, or flattening a ball directly onto the model with a finger. You can also roll out the dough and cut a shape, using a suitably sized cutter.

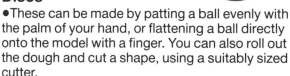

Rolling sausage-shapes

- Break off a piece of dough, then roll it into a ball shape. Either roll the ball gently between the palms of your hands, or place on a smooth surface and roll lightly back and forward.
- Long sausage-shapes can be rolled using two hands at once, with closed fingers. Move from the centre outwards as you roll, to lengthen the dough.
- Or roll with the palm of the hand on first one section, then another, to keep thicknesses even.
- Rolling to a pointed end (for tails etc.) Roll out a sausage shape, then continue to roll at one end only with most pressure on the outside of your palm, until a point is formed. A really fine point can be made by continuing to roll with a finger end.

Rolling out dough

- Form the dough into a rough ball with your cupped hands, then place on a smooth surface. Pat it out into a thick disc with your open palm, then roll your rolling-pin forwards and back using both hands until it becomes the thickness you want. Rolling out on clingfilm helps you turn the dough easily to be rolled in another direction.
- To roll long thin shapes make a sausage shape and roll out as above.

Using cutters

- These should be plastic, not metal. A metal cutter accidentally placed the wrong way up and pressed hard, could result in a cut hand.
- Press the cutter gently into the dough with the flat of your hand, then more firmly once it has bitten. Wriggle it slightly from side to side to make sure it has cut right through.
- Lift off the unwanted dough from round the cut shape. This leaves it free to be lifted elsewhere on a fish slice, or decorated.

Free-hand cutting

This is best done with a round-ended knife, preferably plastic.
- Roll the dough out evenly and draw the shape you want onto it with the knife, before cutting.
- You can use a paper pattern as a guide. Lay it on the dough and cut round it.
- Use a ruler to help you cut straight lines.
- Don't try to turn a corner in the dough with the knife. Make each cut longer than you need, criss-crossing at the corners each time to leave the shape you require (see page 2, caterpillar on a leaf).

Joining pieces of dough

- To make pieces of dough stick together it helps if you scratch both surfaces with your knife and moisten the dough a little with a wet finger.
- You can use a piece cut from a drinking straw to help you join pieces.
- Another way of joining two pieces of dough is to shape one into a point and make a hole in the other piece for a point to fit into.

Decorating dough

This can be done in a variety of ways: poking with fingers, pinching, pressing with various parts of the hand, making imprints with a variety of objects (see tools) or decorating with buttons, beads or pasta. Experiment with anything which makes a sharp outline or interesting shape.

PAPERPLAY

There is a great variety of things you can make using paper or card, scissors and glue, with a few extras. This book is designed to give you some ideas and starting points. Besides being fun, this type of activity can help young children to develop important skills such as hand control and coordination, concentration and decision-making, and broaden their understanding of concepts such as size, shape and measurement.

Bee mobile

You will need: two colours of paper · pencil · ruler · round-ended scissors · paper glue · wool · white paper · felt-tip pen

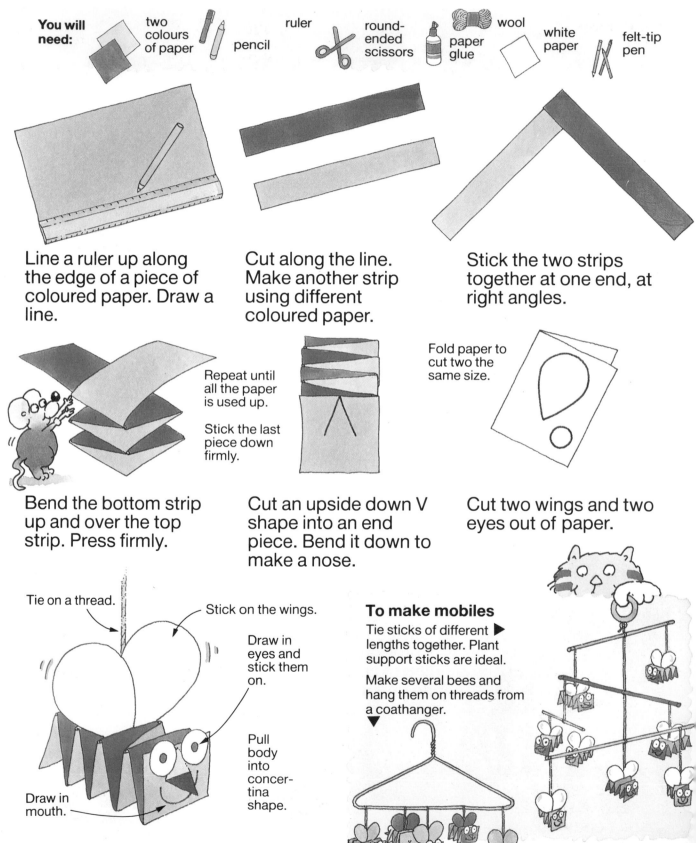

Line a ruler up along the edge of a piece of coloured paper. Draw a line.

Cut along the line. Make another strip using different coloured paper.

Stick the two strips together at one end, at right angles.

Repeat until all the paper is used up.

Stick the last piece down firmly.

Fold paper to cut two the same size.

Bend the bottom strip up and over the top strip. Press firmly.

Cut an upside down V shape into an end piece. Bend it down to make a nose.

Cut two wings and two eyes out of paper.

Tie on a thread.

Stick on the wings.

Draw in eyes and stick them on.

Pull body into concertina shape.

Draw in mouth.

To make mobiles

Tie sticks of different ▶ lengths together. Plant support sticks are ideal.

Make several bees and hang them on threads from a coathanger. ▼

34

Snail mobile

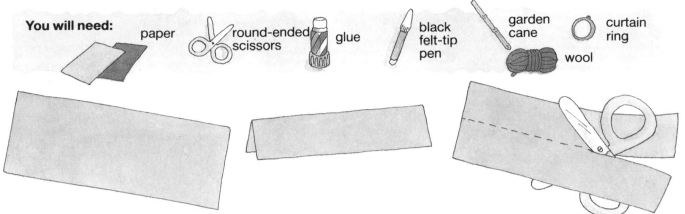

Cut an oblong of paper about 16cm by 3cm (6in by 1in).

Fold it over, long edge to long edge. Press to make a crease.

Open it out and cut along the crease to make two strips.

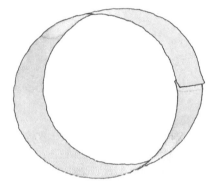

Put glue on one end of one strip. Stick the other end to it to make a circle.

Cut a small square out of the other strip to leave horns. Draw on eyes and a mouth.

Turn it over and put glue on the middle section.

Press firmly to make it stick.

Press the circle onto the glued section of the second strip. Lift up the head end.

Making a mobile

Make several snails and use wool to hang them from a stick as shown.

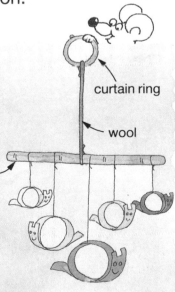

curtain ring

wool

garden cane

Balance the stick by sliding it left or right through the centre loop.

Funny faces

You will need: paper plates, magazines, round-ended scissors, glue, paper or wool

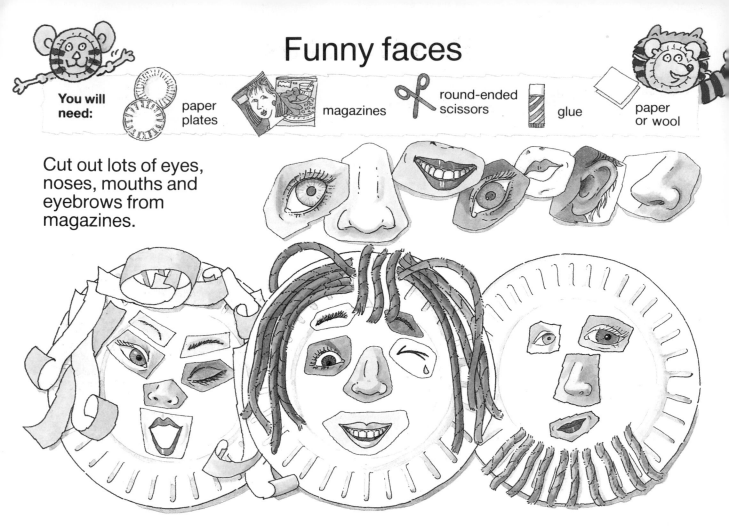

Cut out lots of eyes, noses, mouths and eyebrows from magazines.

Move them around a paper plate until you have the face you want, then stick them down. Add wool or paper hair if you like.

More simple collage ideas

Fridge food

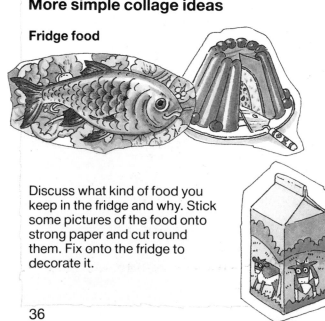

Discuss what kind of food you keep in the fridge and why. Stick some pictures of the food onto strong paper and cut round them. Fix onto the fridge to decorate it.

Car park
Draw out a car park. Discuss how you will arrange and stick down pictures of cars and lorries so they won't block each other in.

Tea table
Stick down paper doilies, or napkins for a tablecloth. Add pictures of cakes, cutlery, cups and plates.

Bendy snakes

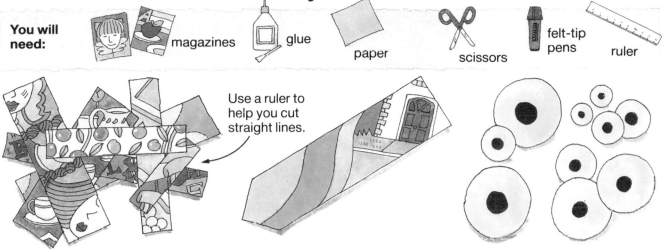

magazines   glue   paper   scissors   felt-tip pens   ruler

Use a ruler to help you cut straight lines.

Cut lots of coloured strips, some wide, some narrow, some long, some short, from a magazine.

Cut one end into a pointed tail, the other into a rounded head.

Draw and cut out lots of eyes. To get two eyes the same size, cut through two layers of paper.

Stick the eyes onto the heads of the snakes.

Turn the snakes over and put blobs of glue down their backs.

Stick them down in loops on paper.

Weave in and out of each other.

37

Trapeze artiste

You will need: wire coathanger, straw, pointed scissors, round-ended scissors, greaseproof paper, sticky tape, decorations (see opposite page), felt-tips, paper-clips

To make the trapeze

Bend a wire coathanger to make a corner about 8cm (3in) from the hook.

Do the same on the other side.

Make some straight sides.

Straighten out the bottom bar.

Cut a piece of straw the same length as the bottom bar. Make a slit along it with pointed scissors*.

Press the straw onto the bottom bar. It should spin freely.

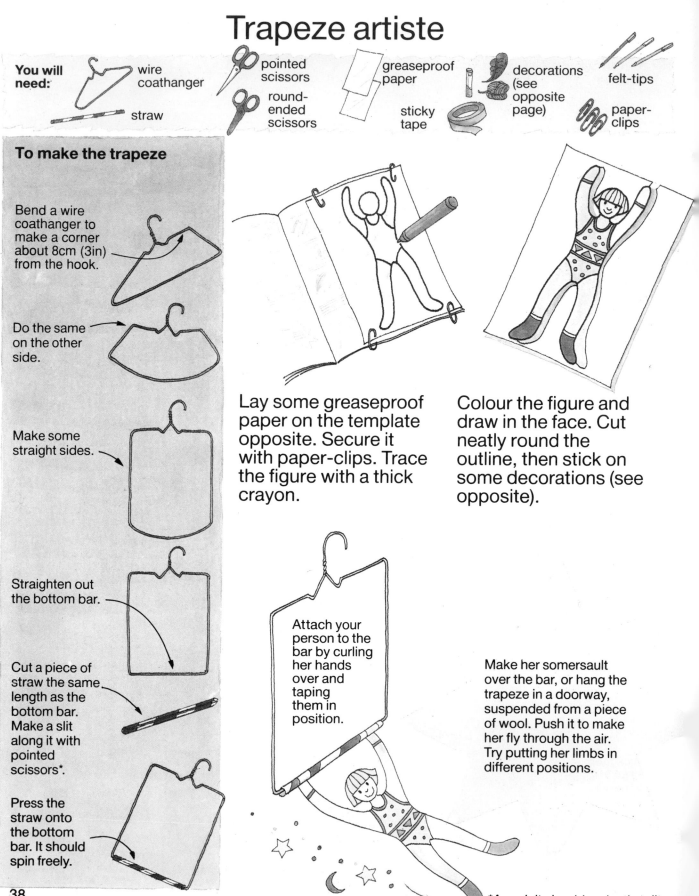

Lay some greaseproof paper on the template opposite. Secure it with paper-clips. Trace the figure with a thick crayon.

Colour the figure and draw in the face. Cut neatly round the outline, then stick on some decorations (see opposite).

Attach your person to the bar by curling her hands over and taping them in position.

Make her somersault over the bar, or hang the trapeze in a doorway, suspended from a piece of wool. Push it to make her fly through the air. Try putting her limbs in different positions.

38

*An adult should make the slit.

Some ideas for decorating the costume

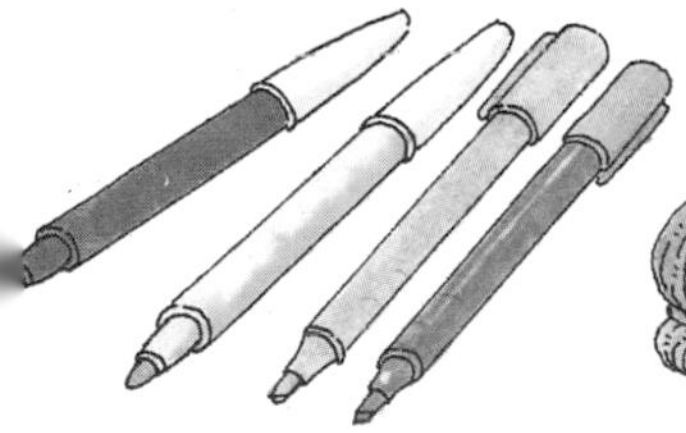

◀ Felt-tip pens

Scraps of wool ▶

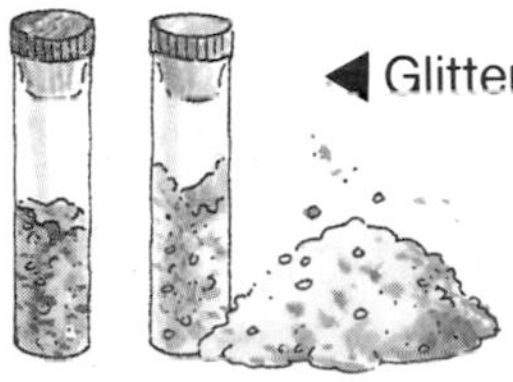

◀ Glitter

Sequins ▶

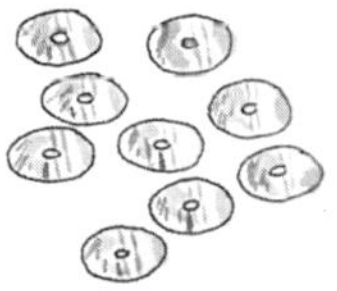

Feathers from a feather duster. ▼

Gummed paper shapes ▲

Ribbon ▶

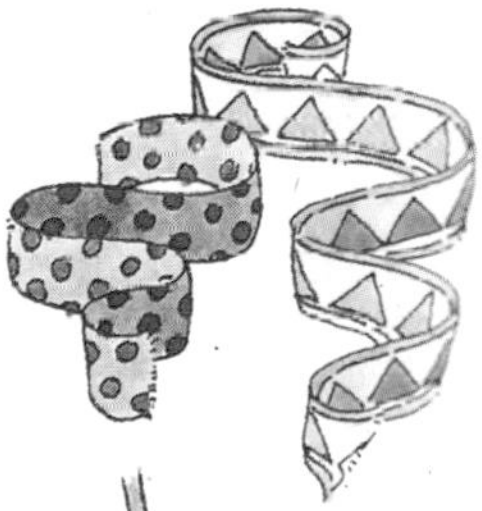

Other ways to decorate your trapeze artiste

Give her wool hair. Only use a little, or the head will be too heavy.

Tie bows round her legs and arms. Use wool or silk thread.

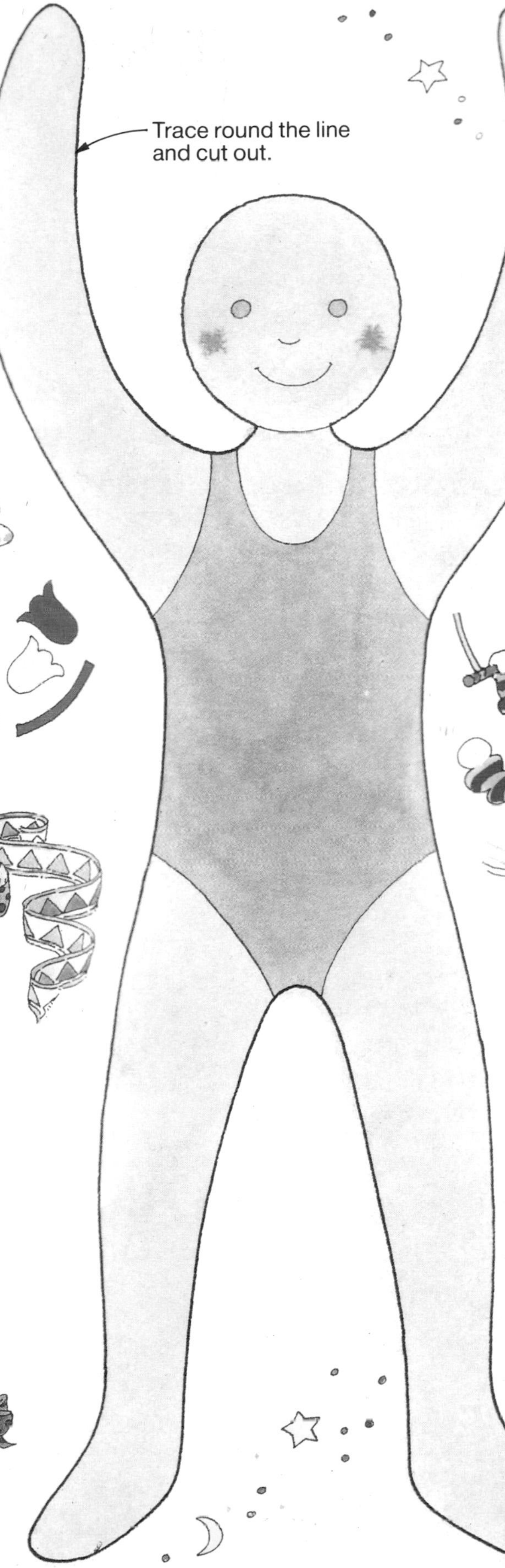

Trace round the line and cut out.

Owl and pussycat

 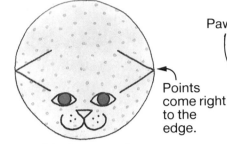
To make the pussycat

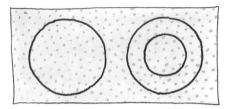

Make two circles on a piece of wallpaper by drawing round a saucer. Cut them out. Inside one, use a jar lid to draw a smaller circle.

Cut two V shapes for the ears in the plain circle. Draw a cat's face on the front half.

Points come right to the edge.

Paws   Tail

Fold the second circle into quarters, then open it out. Draw and cut out two paws and a tail.

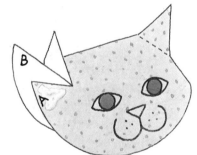

Complete the head by bending up the ears. Glue the underside of point B and overlap onto point A each side.

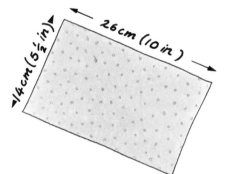

14cm (5½in)   26cm (10in)

Using more wallpaper, draw and cut out a rectangle, 14cm by 26cm (5½in by 10in)

Bend the rectangle into a cylinder, overlapping it by about 2cm (1in). Stick the ends together.

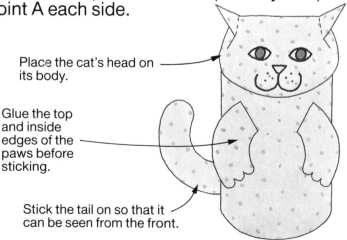

Place the cat's head on its body.

Glue the top and inside edges of the paws before sticking.

Stick the tail on so that it can be seen from the front.

Hint

To make a nice even cylinder shape, wrap the paper strip round a can of food. Stick down the edges, then slide the tin out.

40

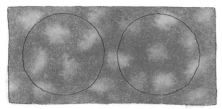 jam-jar lids  felt-tip pens ruler thin, green paper

To make the owl

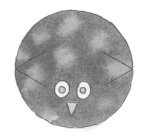

Make two circles on a piece of wallpaper by drawing round a saucer. Cut them out.

On one circle draw and cut out ears. Give your owl large round eyes and a beak.

Fold the other circle in half. Snip with scissors around the lower quarters, then cut down the fold line.

Complete the head as for the cat, but do not bend the ears up.

Cut a rectangle as for the cat. Bend the strip into a cylinder and stick down.

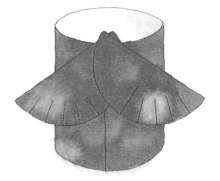

Overlap the wings and stick them together. Stick the wings to the cylinder.

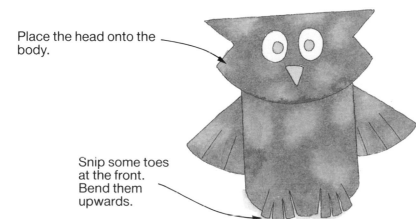

Place the head onto the body.

Snip some toes at the front. Bend them upwards.

Other ideas to try

Make an owl or a cat family. Use jar lids for templates to make kittens and owlets. Make the bodies smaller too.

To make a tree for your owl make a bigger version of the sea anemone on page 43.

41

Magic boxes

You will need:

shoe box with lid · sharp scissors for adults to use · round-ended scissors · sticky tape · felt-tip pens · paints and large brushes · thread · straws

Flying ghost box

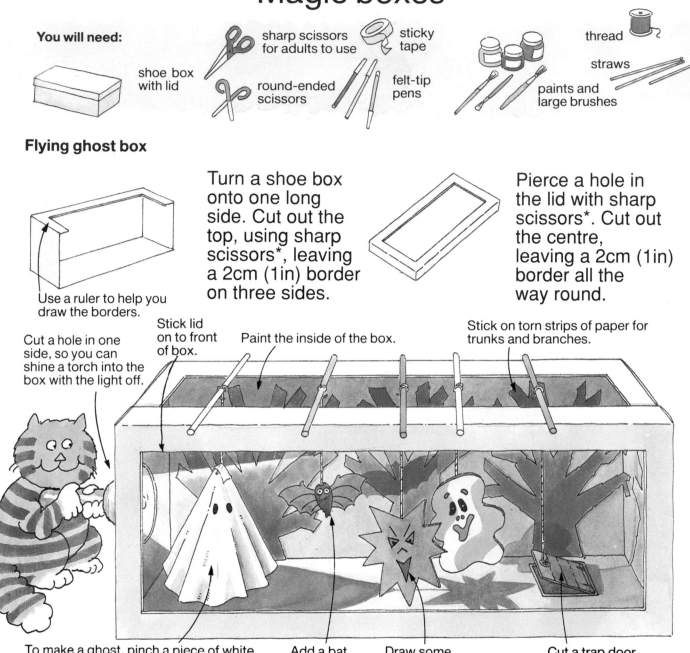

Turn a shoe box onto one long side. Cut out the top, using sharp scissors*, leaving a 2cm (1in) border on three sides.

Pierce a hole in the lid with sharp scissors*. Cut out the centre, leaving a 2cm (1in) border all the way round.

Use a ruler to help you draw the borders.

Cut a hole in one side, so you can shine a torch into the box with the light off.

Stick lid on to front of box.

Paint the inside of the box.

Stick on torn strips of paper for trunks and branches.

To make a ghost, pinch a piece of white toilet tissue in the centre, so that the corners hang down. Draw on black eyes. Hang from a thread fastened to a straw.

Add a bat to swoop around.

Draw some strange shapes for spooks. Colour them and cut them out. Hang them from straws.

Cut a trap door out of paper. Stick one side to the floor, so that it can move up and down.

Jumping-up skeleton

Draw a skeleton on white paper and then cut an outline round it.

Fold it as shown and attach a thread to the back of its head with sticky tape.

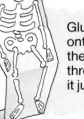

Glue the bottom onto the floor of the box. Pull the thread to make it jump up.

42

An adult should do the cutting.

glue

paper

cereal-box cardboard

torch

white toilet tissue

clingfilm

cellophane

sponge

pebbles

sand

shells

Aquarium

Cut out the side of the box and the lid as for the ghost box.

Paint blue water and a yellow, sandy floor inside the box.

Use tape to stick clingfilm over the inside of the lid, so that it looks like glass.

Glue or tape the lid onto the front.

Stick torn coloured strips onto the sides to make seaweed or coral.

Draw fish on card or paper. Colour both sides and cut out. Attach thread and hang from straws.

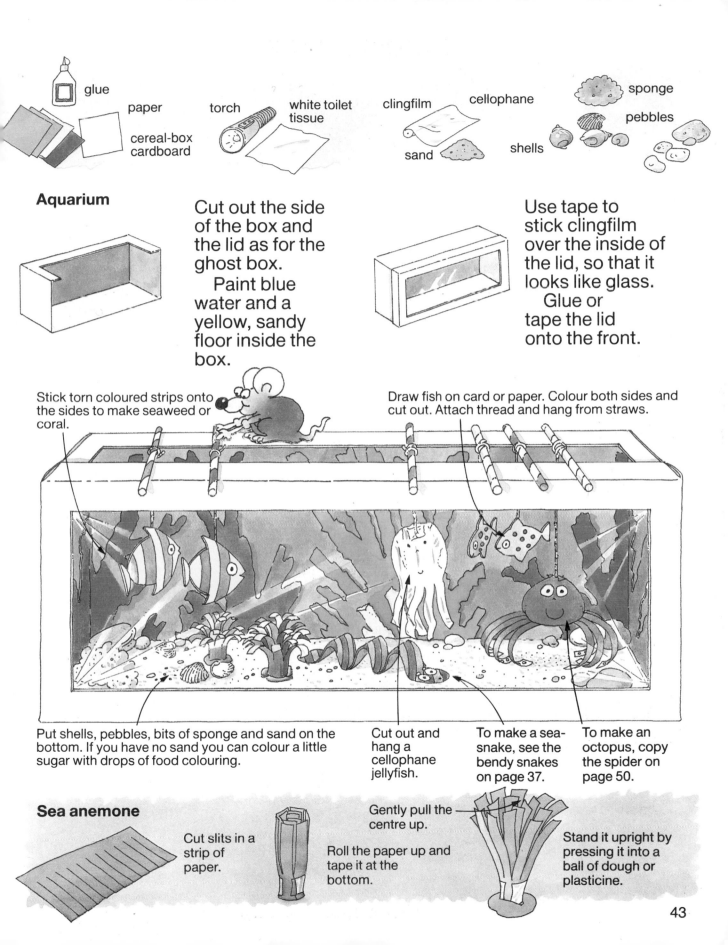

Put shells, pebbles, bits of sponge and sand on the bottom. If you have no sand you can colour a little sugar with drops of food colouring.

Cut out and hang a cellophane jellyfish.

To make a sea-snake, see the bendy snakes on page 37.

To make an octopus, copy the spider on page 50.

Sea anemone

Cut slits in a strip of paper.

Roll the paper up and tape it at the bottom.

Gently pull the centre up.

Stand it upright by pressing it into a ball of dough or plasticine.

43

Super-glider

Measure and cut a rectangle 10cm by 15cm (4in by 6in). Make a crease down the centre by folding it in half. Open it out and turn it over.

Turn the top corners down, so that the points meet in the centre.

Turn the top triangle down.

Turn the top corners down, so the points meet in the centre.

Turn the two top sides of the triangle in, so the points meet in the centre.

Fold in half, along the original centre crease.

Turn upside down. Pull the wings up until they are level. Hold between your finger and thumb underneath and launch.

Windmill

Cut a square of paper, 10cm by 10cm (4in by 4in).

Fold diagonally to make creases.

Cut from each corner along the creases, almost to the centre.

Glue and turn up every other point. Stick them together in the centre, overlapping slightly.

Press a large-headed pin through the centre of the windmill and into the top of a straw. Blow hard to make it whirl, or hold it in a strong wind.

44

Submarine

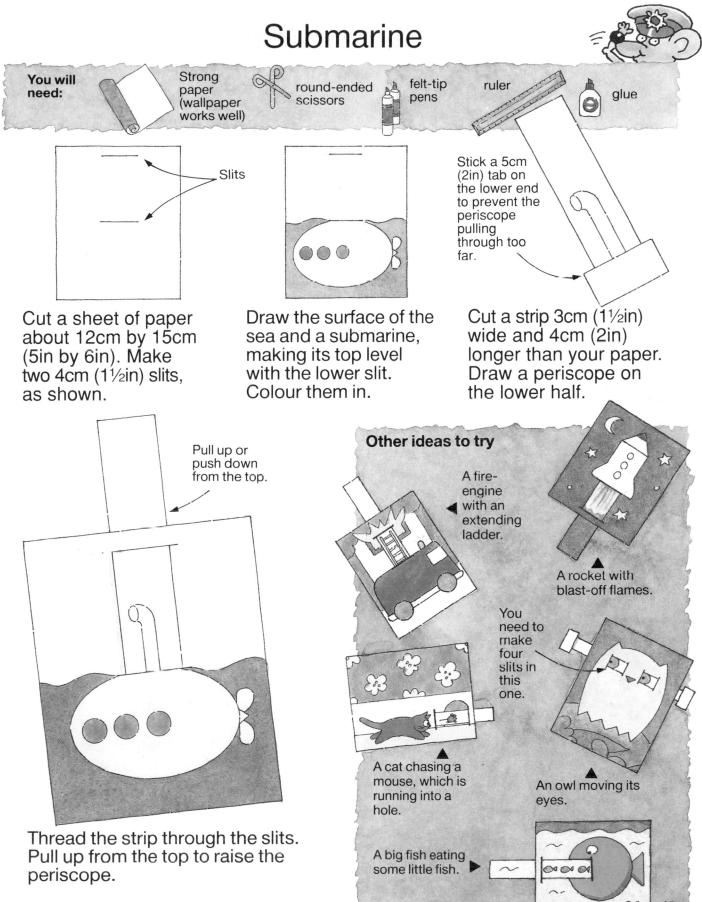

You will need: Strong paper (wallpaper works well), round-ended scissors, felt-tip pens, ruler, glue

Cut a sheet of paper about 12cm by 15cm (5in by 6in). Make two 4cm (1½in) slits, as shown.

Slits

Draw the surface of the sea and a submarine, making its top level with the lower slit. Colour them in.

Cut a strip 3cm (1½in) wide and 4cm (2in) longer than your paper. Draw a periscope on the lower half.

Stick a 5cm (2in) tab on the lower end to prevent the periscope pulling through too far.

Pull up or push down from the top.

Thread the strip through the slits. Pull up from the top to raise the periscope.

Other ideas to try

A fire-engine with an extending ladder.

A rocket with blast-off flames.

You need to make four slits in this one.

A cat chasing a mouse, which is running into a hole.

An owl moving its eyes.

A big fish eating some little fish.

45

Cars and roads

You will need: stiff paper   round-ended scissors   felt-tip pens or paints

Draw cars, lorries, motorbikes, bicycles, trees, shops etc. along the straight edges of your paper. Colour them in bright colours.

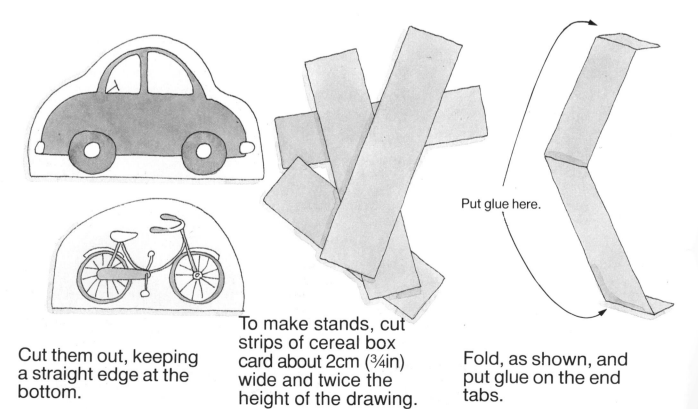

Put glue here.

Cut them out, keeping a straight edge at the bottom.

To make stands, cut strips of cereal box card about 2cm (¾in) wide and twice the height of the drawing.

Fold, as shown, and put glue on the end tabs.

46

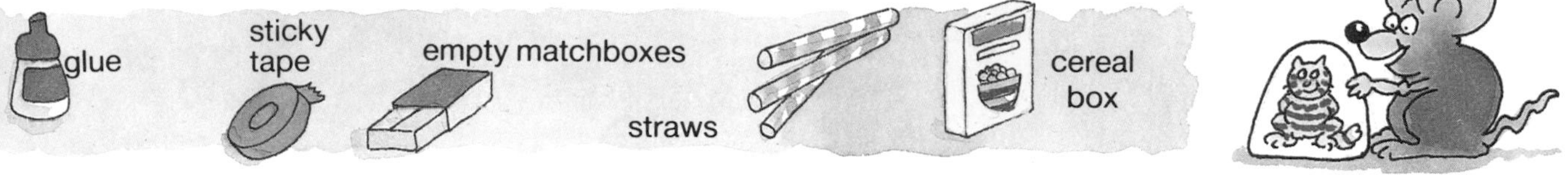

glue

sticky tape

empty matchboxes

straws

cereal box

Use two stands for wide pictures.

To make road signs and bridges, see below.

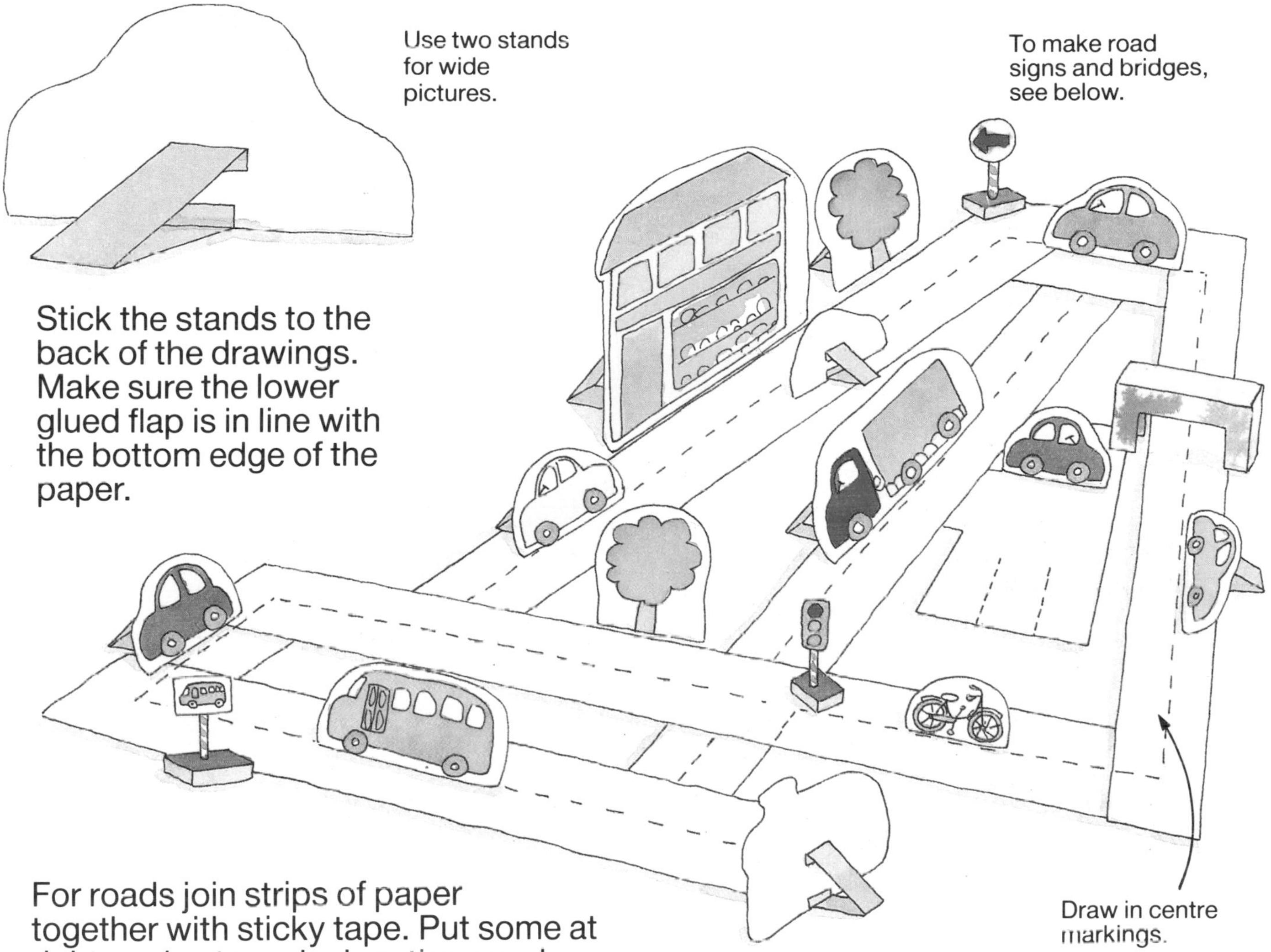

Stick the stands to the back of the drawings. Make sure the lower glued flap is in line with the bottom edge of the paper.

For roads join strips of paper together with sticky tape. Put some at right angles to make junctions and corners.

Draw in centre markings.

Other ideas to try

Road signs

Draw and cut out road signs.

Stick a cut-down straw to the back.

Make a hole in a matchbox with a pencil point. Push the straw into the hole.

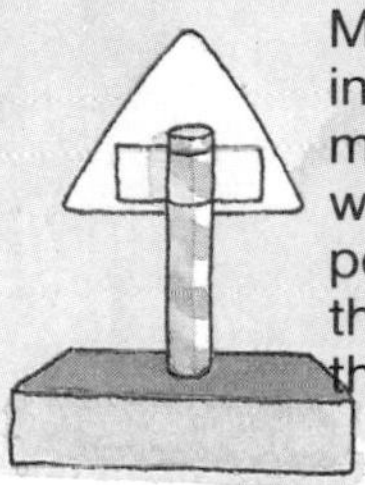

Bridge

Cut a cereal box in half. Cut a rectangle wider than the road from each side.

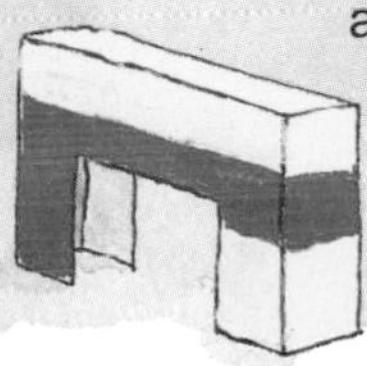

Animal zoo

Draw and cut out lots of different animals and fix them onto stands, as for the cars and buildings above.

Paper money and wallet

You will need: white paper · felt-tip pens or crayons · coloured paper · sticky tape · glue · soft pencil · coins · ruler

Cut out some pieces of paper the size and shape of money notes. On each one write a number to show how much it is worth and draw a picture.

For your wallet, cut a piece of coloured paper 2cm (¾in) wider than your paper money and one and a half times as high.

Fold up the bottom edge by about a third.

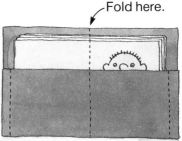

Fold here.

Stick down the sides to make a pocket. Put the money in it and fold it in half.

Write your name on the front and then decorate it.

Other ideas to try

Coins
Lay thin paper over real coins. Hold it firmly in place while you rub over them with a soft pencil. Stick card on the back and cut them out.

Stamps
Draw a small box. Draw or stick a small picture in the centre. Cut it out.

Envelopes
Fold a square of paper diagonally in both directions. Open it out.

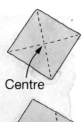

Centre

Fold the bottom corner up to the centre. Fold in each of the two side corners, overlapping the edges slightly.

Glue or tape down the edges. Fold the remaining top corner down to make the flap.

Racing rafts

You will need: clingfilm, corrugated paper or card, straws, pencil, coloured paper, felt-tip pens, round-ended scissors, ruler, glue, page from glossy magazine, sticky tape

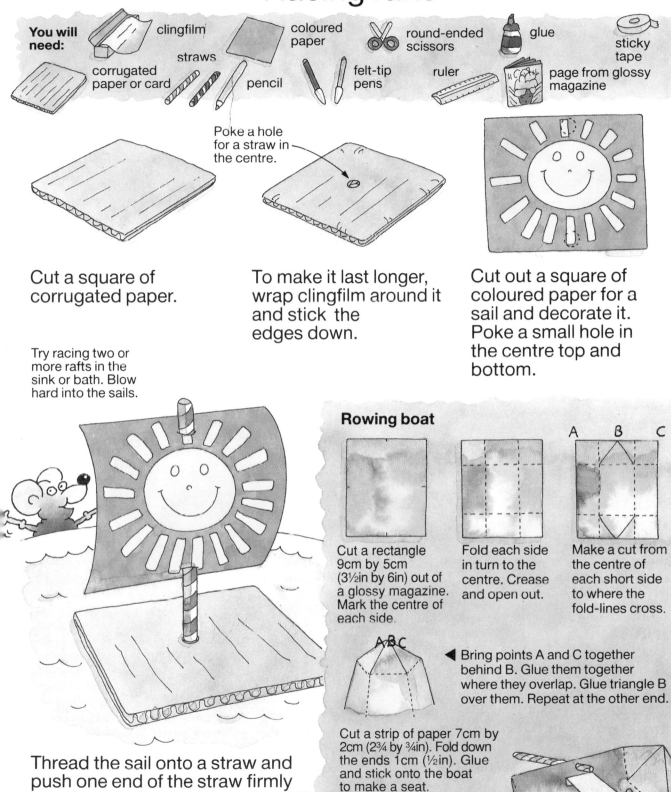

Poke a hole for a straw in the centre.

Cut a square of corrugated paper.

To make it last longer, wrap clingfilm around it and stick the edges down.

Cut out a square of coloured paper for a sail and decorate it. Poke a small hole in the centre top and bottom.

Try racing two or more rafts in the sink or bath. Blow hard into the sails.

Thread the sail onto a straw and push one end of the straw firmly into the raft. Cut the straw down if necessary.

Rowing boat

Cut a rectangle 9cm by 5cm (3½in by 6in) out of a glossy magazine. Mark the centre of each side.

Fold each side in turn to the centre. Crease and open out.

Make a cut from the centre of each short side to where the fold-lines cross.

Bring points A and C together behind B. Glue them together where they overlap. Glue triangle B over them. Repeat at the other end.

Cut a strip of paper 7cm by 2cm (2¾ by ¾in). Fold down the ends 1cm (½in). Glue and stick onto the boat to make a seat.

Cut some straws and poke through the side for oars.

49

Paper puppets

You will need: coloured crêpe paper · paper to crumple · round-ended scissors · sticky tape · felt-tip pens · wool or elastic · glue · straws · paper

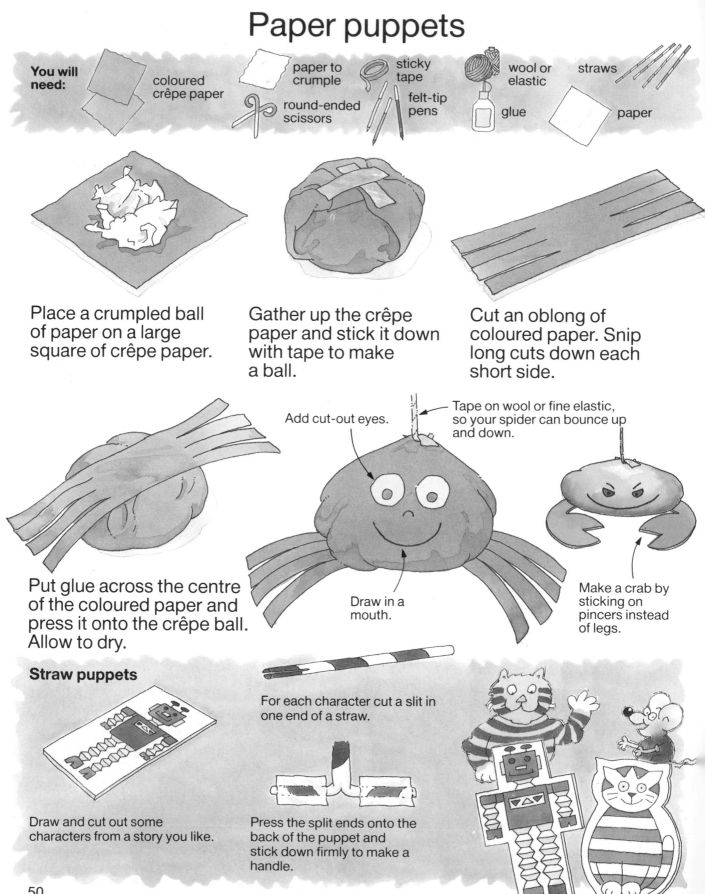

Place a crumpled ball of paper on a large square of crêpe paper.

Gather up the crêpe paper and stick it down with tape to make a ball.

Cut an oblong of coloured paper. Snip long cuts down each short side.

Put glue across the centre of the coloured paper and press it onto the crêpe ball. Allow to dry.

Add cut-out eyes.

Tape on wool or fine elastic, so your spider can bounce up and down.

Draw in a mouth.

Make a crab by sticking on pincers instead of legs.

Straw puppets

Draw and cut out some characters from a story you like.

For each character cut a slit in one end of a straw.

Press the split ends onto the back of the puppet and stick down firmly to make a handle.

50

You will need:

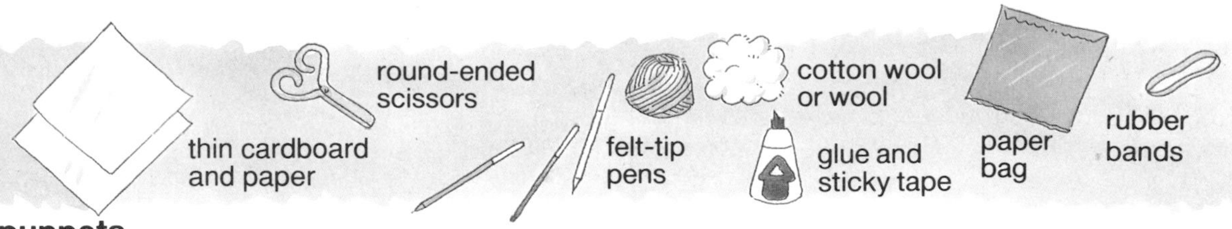

thin cardboard and paper

round-ended scissors

felt-tip pens

cotton wool or wool

glue and sticky tape

paper bag

rubber bands

Dancing puppets

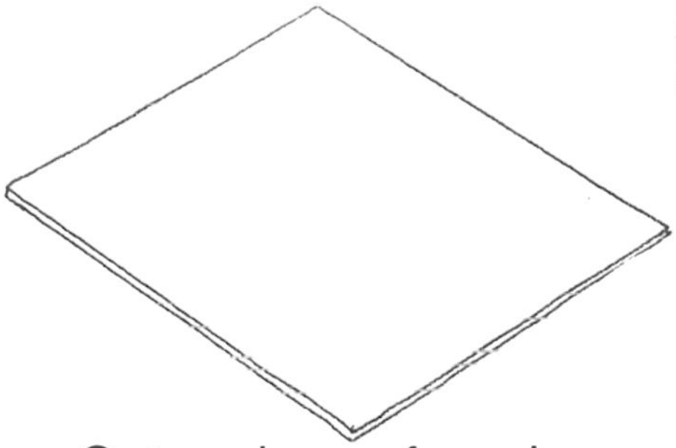

Round off the top with scissors.

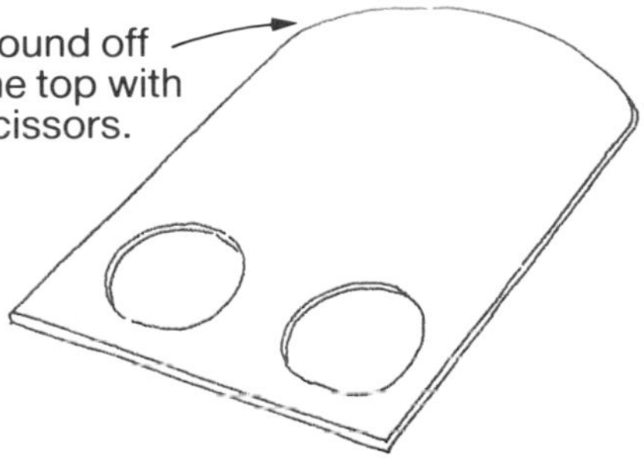

Cut a piece of card 2cm (1in) wider than the width of two fingers.

Make two holes near the bottom to poke your fingers through.

Draw on faces.

Stick on cotton wool or wool hair.

Push just past second joint.

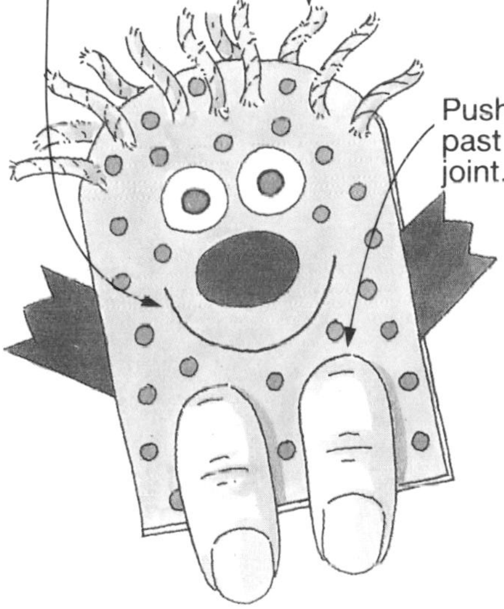

Push your fingers through the back and make your puppet dance around.

Paper-bag puppets

Draw a face on one side of an upside down paper bag.

Twist the corners for ears. Put your hand in the bag and fix round your wrist with a rubber band.

Finger-end puppets

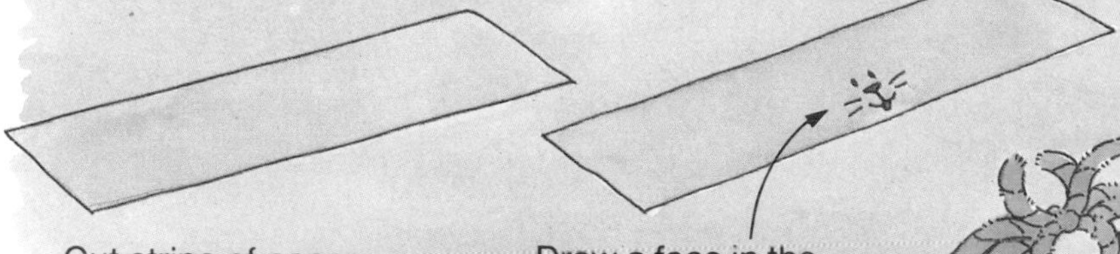

Cut strips of paper about 2cm (1in) wide by 5cm (2in) long.

Draw a face in the centre of each strip.

Bend the strips round the ends of your fingers and stick to fit.

Add some hair.

Add some ears.

Costumes and disguises

You will need:

pencil

paper plates 18cm (7in) diameter

round-ended scissors

felt-tip pen

yoghurt carton

sticky tape or glue

wool

doily

Mr Wolf mask

Cut holes for your eyes and a space for your nose, in a paper plate.

Cut a section from a yoghurt pot, as shown.

Tape or glue the yoghurt pot onto the plate, cut side downwards.

Add ears and a nose cut from stiff paper. Trim away sharp edges, so you can speak easily.

Trim here

Cut along lines.

Fold some paper as shown and cut along lines to make teeth.

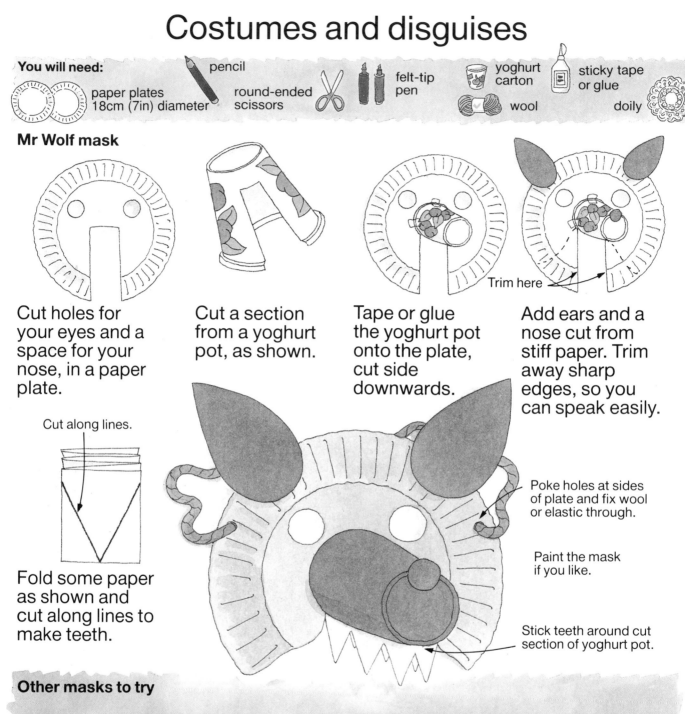

Poke holes at sides of plate and fix wool or elastic through.

Paint the mask if you like.

Stick teeth around cut section of yoghurt pot.

Other masks to try

The three little pigs
Cut a yoghurt pot down to make a snout. Stick on as for the wolf. Draw in nostrils and paint. Add ears. Trim the sharp edges.

Goldilocks and the three bears
Cut the centre out of a doily to make a lace collar for Goldilocks.

Make the bears' ears round. Stick on noses. Trim sharp edges.

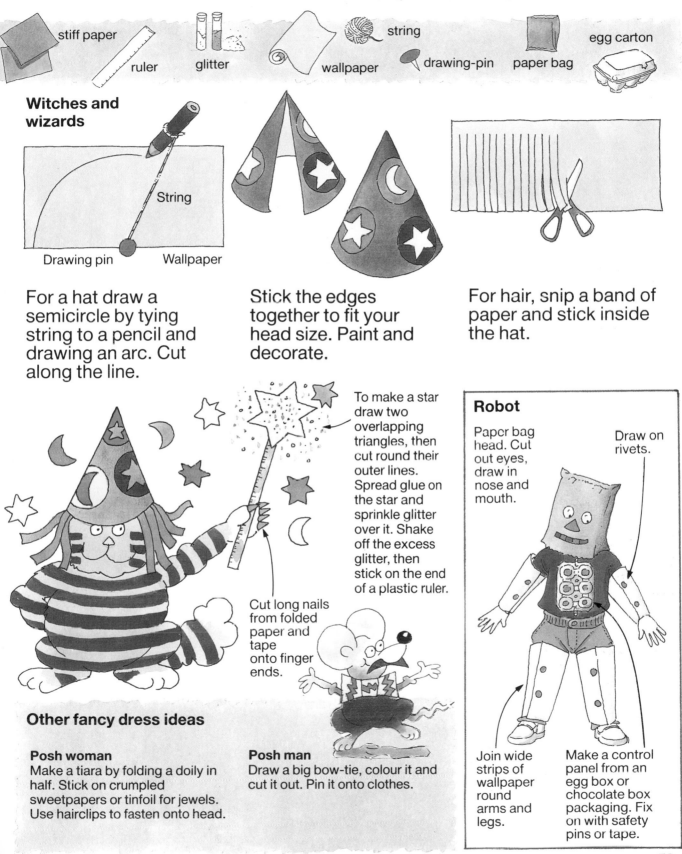

stiff paper
ruler
glitter
string
wallpaper
drawing-pin
paper bag
egg carton

Witches and wizards

String

Drawing pin   Wallpaper

For a hat draw a semicircle by tying string to a pencil and drawing an arc. Cut along the line.

Stick the edges together to fit your head size. Paint and decorate.

For hair, snip a band of paper and stick inside the hat.

To make a star draw two overlapping triangles, then cut round their outer lines. Spread glue on the star and sprinkle glitter over it. Shake off the excess glitter, then stick on the end of a plastic ruler.

Cut long nails from folded paper and tape onto finger ends.

Robot

Paper bag head. Cut out eyes, draw in nose and mouth.

Draw on rivets.

Join wide strips of wallpaper round arms and legs.

Make a control panel from an egg box or chocolate box packaging. Fix on with safety pins or tape.

Other fancy dress ideas

Posh woman
Make a tiara by folding a doily in half. Stick on crumpled sweetpapers or tinfoil for jewels. Use hairclips to fasten onto head.

Posh man
Draw a big bow-tie, colour it and cut it out. Pin it onto clothes.

Surprise doors

On a big piece of paper draw a large castle or house, with plenty of doors and windows.

Cut round the doors and windows, so they will open and shut.

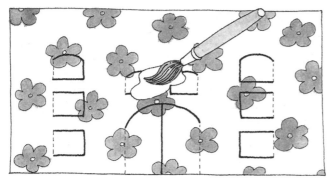

Cover the back of the picture, except the doors and windows, with paste. Stick it down onto the white side of another piece of wallpaper. Leave it to dry.

Open up the doors and windows so you can draw what's going on inside. Make up a story about it.

Other ideas to try

Kitchen
Make a kitchen with fridge, cupboards, washing machine and freezer.

Show what is inside each of them.

Ship
Make a ship with big portholes that will open and shut.

Show what the sailors, passengers and captain are all doing.

Family portrait book

You will need:
wallpaper or sugar paper   glue   round-ended scissors   felt-tip pens   white drawing paper

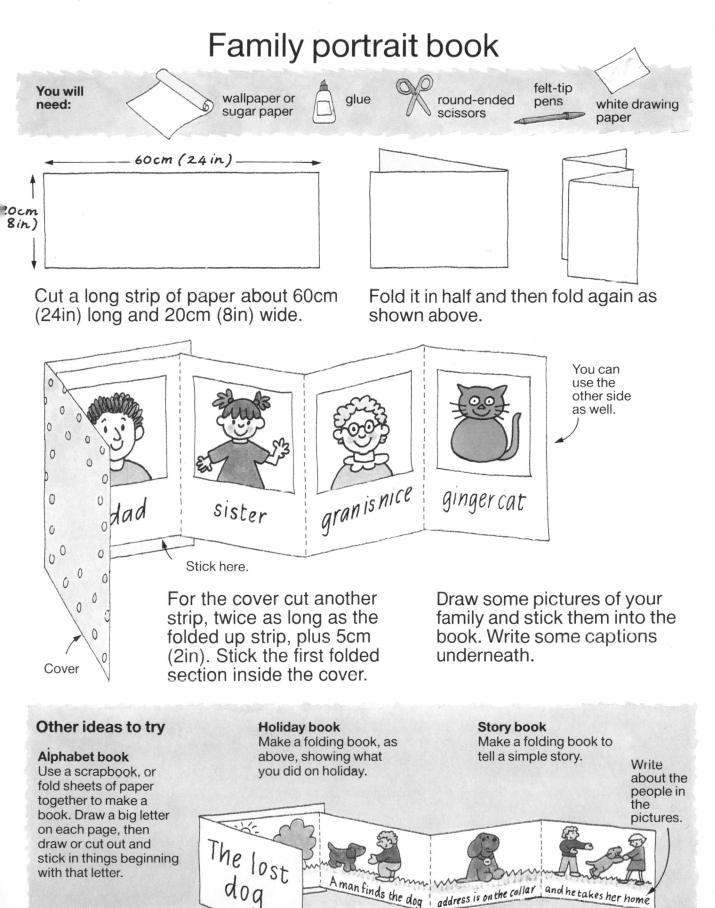

← 60cm (24in) →

20cm (8in)

Cut a long strip of paper about 60cm (24in) long and 20cm (8in) wide.

Fold it in half and then fold again as shown above.

You can use the other side as well.

dad   sister   gran is nice   ginger cat

Stick here.

Cover

For the cover cut another strip, twice as long as the folded up strip, plus 5cm (2in). Stick the first folded section inside the cover.

Draw some pictures of your family and stick them into the book. Write some captions underneath.

Other ideas to try

Alphabet book
Use a scrapbook, or fold sheets of paper together to make a book. Draw a big letter on each page, then draw or cut out and stick in things beginning with that letter.

Holiday book
Make a folding book, as above, showing what you did on holiday.

Story book
Make a folding book to tell a simple story.

Write about the people in the pictures.

The lost dog

A man finds the dog   address is on the collar   and he takes her home

Jewellery

Straw beads

Cut strips of patterned paper the length of a straw and about 8cm (3in) wide. Cover them with glue on the plain side.

Lay a straw on one long edge and roll the paper round it as firmly as you can. Leave to dry. Repeat this process several times.

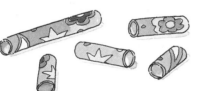

Cut the straw beads into any length you like. If the ends flatten squeeze them into round shapes again.

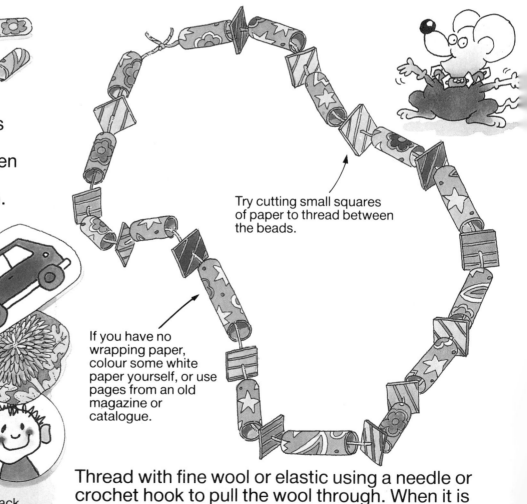

Try cutting small squares of paper to thread between the beads.

If you have no wrapping paper, colour some white paper yourself, or use pages from an old magazine or catalogue.

Brooches

Draw or cut out pictures you like to stick onto cereal-box card.

Attach a safety pin at the back with tape to make a brooch.

Thread with fine wool or elastic using a needle or crochet hook to pull the wool through. When it is long enough to slip over your head, tie in a knot.

cereal packet

safety pin

sticky tape

small jar lid

round-ended scissors

Matching earrings

Wrapping paper

Jar lid

Strip of glue

Draw round a small jar lid to make a circle. Cut the circle out.

Fold the circle in half, then cut along the fold line.

Put a strip of glue halfway along each straight edge on the wrong side.

Bend round and overlap the edges to make a cone. Stick down firmly. Snip the top off the cone.

Loop some wool through the cone using a crochet hook or hair clip to help you thread it through.

Stick the ends inside the cone, leaving the loops to hang over your ears.

Ideas for bracelets

Cut two strips of different-coloured paper, one to fit round your wrist and one much longer.

Make a long concertina shape, by folding two bits of paper across each other at right angles. Stick into a circle.

Make a bracelet using straw beads threaded onto string or elastic.

Wrap the long piece round the short piece to give a striped effect. Join the ends with sticky tape to make a circle. Glue down the ends and trim.

57

Greetings cards

You will need: white paper · stiff, coloured paper · felt-tip pens or crayons · round-ended scissors

Pop-up cards

Cut an oblong piece of paper (A) and fold the longest sides in half.

Press firmly along the folds to make a crease.

Cut a strip (B) about 3cm (1in) wide and half the length of A. Fold in half.

Open it out, turn it over, fold each end up about 1cm (½in). Glue each end.

Put glue on this side.

Lift the top half of A towards you so that B stands out.

When you open the card the picture will pop up.

Lay B down the centre of A, glue side down, so that the creases exactly correspond.

Colour and cut out a picture to cover the lower half of B. Stick it on.

Write your message here.

Name cards

Make an oblong card long enough to write your chosen name in big letters. Write the name onto it.

Stick little pieces of screwed-up sweet wrappers or tissue over the letters you have drawn. You can also make them into patterns.

Ian

glue

tissue paper
or sweetpapers

old photos

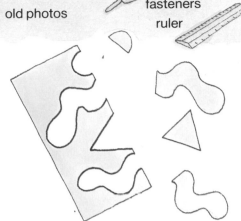
paper
fasteners
ruler

Contrast cards

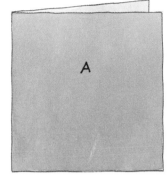

Fold an oblong piece
of paper in half to
make a card (A).

Cut another piece (B),
half the width of the
front, in a different
colour.

Cut deep shapes from
the right-hand side of
(B). Save all the pieces
you have cut.

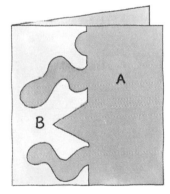

Stick (B) onto the front
left half of (A).

Turn over the cut-out pieces and stick them down
opposite the corresponding shapes, so that they
mirror each other.

Other ideas for cards

Paper fastener cards
Use paper fasteners to fix
separate parts, such as ears or
wheels onto your cards. Poke
the holes first with a pencil.

Photo cards
Cut some faces of your family
from unwanted photos. They
can be quite small.

Stick them onto a card, then
draw a picture round them.

59

Paper presents

You will need:  paper,  felt-tip pens, round-ended scissors, old magazines, glue

Hand bookmark

Draw round your hand with a felt-tip pen.

Colour the hand brightly.

Cut it out carefully.

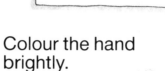

Willy worm bookmark

Draw, colour and cut out a worm. He should be longer than the height of a book so that his head and tail will stick out.

Give your worm some clothes, or draw on things like glasses or a bowtie.

Stick onto a strip of paper and use it to put in a book so that the fingers show your place.

cereal box

clingfilm

sticky tape

wallpaper paste (non-fungicidal)

wallpaper brush

yoghurt pot

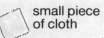
small piece of cloth

Mosaic place mat

Cut a large rectangle from a cereal box. Round off the corners with scissors.

Use a felt-tip pen to draw a big, bold design.

Find the colours you want to use in magazines. Tear them into pieces about 2cm (1in) square. Keep the colours separate.

Stick the coloured pieces onto the design.

Cover your dry mat with clingfilm taped on at the back.

Other ideas to try

Needle case
Fold a piece of stiff paper double to make a card. Draw a butterfly on it making sure the wings go right to the edge of the paper. Colour or decorate brightly and cut out double, so that it opens out.

Glue a small piece of cloth at the top only and stick onto the right side, for keeping needles in.

Write or copy your message on the left.

Pencil holder
Cover a yoghurt pot or cut-down plastic bottle with paper from an old comic or toy catalogue.

Hints

It is easier to paste the mat than the small bits of paper.

The more shades of each colour you use, the better the result.

61

Paper bowls

You will need: cardboard egg carton · cereal bowl and plate* · old tea towel · clingfilm · round-ended scissors · electric food mixer · sieve · large bowl

Tear the egg box into pieces and soak in warm water in a large bowl until soft (10-20 mins.).

If you haven't got a mixer, squash the pieces up with your hands.

Tip some of the water into the food mixer. Switch it on and add the pieces gradually until you have a watery, mushy pulp.

Tip the mixture into a fine-mesh sieve over the sink. Press down to squeeze out most of the water.

Cover the bowl completely.

Place the upturned cereal bowl onto a plate. Cover it with clingfilm. Press small lumps of paper pulp all over it.

Place the tea towel over the bowl and press firmly all over, to flatten the pulp and remove excess water.

Use oven gloves to take it out.

Leave to dry in a warm place, or put in a microwave oven* and cook on a high setting for 10-12 mins., or until it is dry.

When the pulp has dried, remove it from the cereal bowl and trim round the edge with some scissors.

Paint and decorate your bowl with poster paints.

Other ideas to try

Try using egg boxes of two or more different colours in your bowls.

To make a stronger bowl, try kneading a little non-fungicidal wallpaper paste into the pulp after sieving.

62

*When using a microwave use only bowls and plates recommended for microwave use.

Materials and skills

The main equipment you will need to make the things shown in this book are paper, scissors, glue and felt-tip pens or paints. This page gives you advice on what type of glue, paper and scissors to use. The following page provides some tips and hints on cutting, folding and measuring.

The specific things you will need for each project are listed at the top of each page.

Scissors

All-plastic scissors can be fragile and not so good for use on stiffer papers or thin card. All-metal scissors can be heavy and awkward for children to use.

A good compromise is a pair of plastic scissors with a metal blade. These are often brightly-coloured and made in the shape of a bird, animal or fish.

Scissors should always be round-ended for safety and any adult's scissors should be put away out of reach immediately after use.

Glue

•Glue sticks are clean to use, with the gum easily directed to where you want it to go. Be sure to put the cap back after use. They can dry out quickly.

•Liquid glues and gums are useful and spread easily, but take longer to dry.

•P.V.A. (polyvinyl acetate) is good for sticking large areas. It is white but dries transparent. Protect clothing with aprons. Roll up sleeves. Wash brushes out carefully after use.

•Wallpaper paste is also good for large areas. It is very cheap and you can make up small batches as you need it. For safety always use the non-fungicidal type. If you have some left over, cover it with clingfilm and store in the fridge for use another day.

•Flour-and-water paste can be made up by making up a smooth paste, bringing to the boil and simmering for a few minutes. Make sure it is quite cool before use.

•Sticky tape is invaluable but can be tricky. Cut several strips and attach lightly at one end only to a suitable work-top edge ready for use.

Do not use solvent-based glues or instant bond glue.

Paper

White paper – use sheets from a writing pad, typing paper, drawer or wall lining paper, or other similar paper.

Stiff paper – use wallpaper or the covers of magazines.

Strong paper – wallpaper is fairly strong.

Thin, strong paper – typing paper, or something similar.

Dark or coloured paper – sugar paper, paper from magazines or wrapping paper.

Card – use cut-up cereal boxes or something similar.

Collecting a supply of paper

You can collect most of the paper you need for these projects, without having to buy anything specially.

It is a good idea to keep a drawer or box in which to store all the odd bits you manage to find.

Below is a list of things it is worth saving.

•coloured foil or cellophane sweet wrappers

•clear cellophane from flowers and boxes of pasta

•tissue paper from fruit or packaging

•thin cardboard - use cut-up cereal boxes or something similar.

•brightly-coloured pages from glossy magazines, leaflets or comics

•out-of-date catalogues

•corrugated paper is often used to pack china

•wrapping paper from birthdays or Christmas

•wallpaper is invaluable for its pattern value and strength and for its possibilities as drawing or painting paper

Materials and skills

Other good things to have

doilies

crêpe paper

drinking straws

paper plates

empty yoghurt cartons

cardboard egg boxes

wire coathangers

clingfilm

pencils

ruler

wool

Folding paper

Folding is often repetitive, so you could do one fold and let your child copy you.

Point out before each step which edge is to be lined up with which. Show your child how to hold them firmly down while pressing in the crease.

Encourage her to check each time that the result looks like the drawing.

Measuring

Making things from paper provides good opportunities for learning about measuring.

You will probably need to do any accurate measuring required yourself, but your child can learn a lot from watching you, especially if you explain carefully what you are doing.

When she is ready to try measuring for herself, show her how to line the ruler up accurately and mark off the required length with a pencil.

Using scissors

This may take a little time for a child to master. To begin with she could be encouraged to cut along straight lines. Let her draw some herself on newspaper, using a ruler. She could then progress to curved lines. Draw round a dinner plate to start with, then progress to a tea plate, where the curve will be sharper and so on.

On larger projects take it in turns to do the cutting. As she becomes ready for them, show your child the techniques explained in the next column.

Cutting round a shape

● Always cut a rough outline first, this takes away an unmanageable mass of paper.

● Encourage your child to hold the paper lightly with her free hand near to where she will cut, to avoid tearing.

● Explain that she should not pull on the paper, the scissors should do the work.

● Demonstrate how to line up the blades of the scissors along the line to be cut to make it as accurate as possible.

Cutting out a shape

● Poke a hole in the centre of the shape to be removed with the pointed end of a pencil.

● Insert the lower blade of the scissors into the hole and cut to the edge of the shape.

● Cut round it carefully and remove it.

● If the paper is too stiff cut a slit in the paper by bending, rather than creasing the paper in the centre of the unwanted area. Make a cut into the folded edge, open out and insert the scissors. Cut to the edge.

ODDS & ENDS

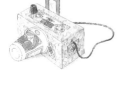

There is a great variety of things you can make using odds and ends from around the house. This book is designed to give you some ideas and starting points. Besides providing enjoyment and satisfaction, this type of activity can help young children to develop skills such as hand control and co-ordination, concentration and decision-making, and broaden their understanding of concepts such as size, shape, space and measurement.

Post box

You will need:
poster paint, thick black felt-tip pen, tall box or cylinder, breadknife, ball-point pen, bowl, large paintbrushes, large bottle cap

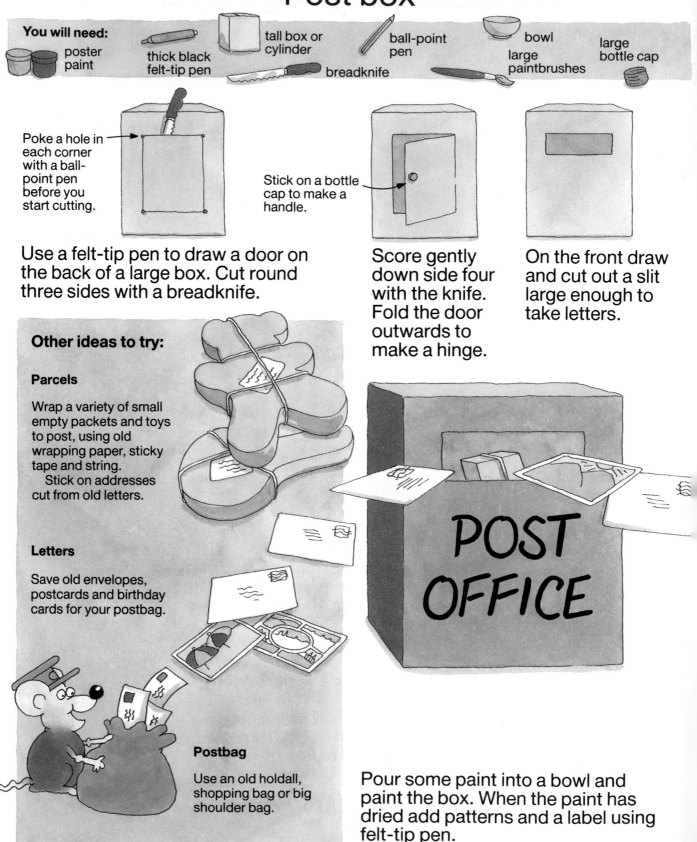

Poke a hole in each corner with a ball-point pen before you start cutting.

Use a felt-tip pen to draw a door on the back of a large box. Cut round three sides with a breadknife.

Stick on a bottle cap to make a handle.

Score gently down side four with the knife. Fold the door outwards to make a hinge.

On the front draw and cut out a slit large enough to take letters.

Other ideas to try:

Parcels

Wrap a variety of small empty packets and toys to post, using old wrapping paper, sticky tape and string.
   Stick on addresses cut from old letters.

Letters

Save old envelopes, postcards and birthday cards for your postbag.

Postbag

Use an old holdall, shopping bag or big shoulder bag.

POST OFFICE

Pour some paint into a bowl and paint the box. When the paint has dried add patterns and a label using felt-tip pen.

Ink-pad and franking stamp

You will need: scissors — screw-top bottle cap — plastic lid or saucer — thin sponge about 4cm by 4cm (2in by 2in) — elastic band — glue — poster paint

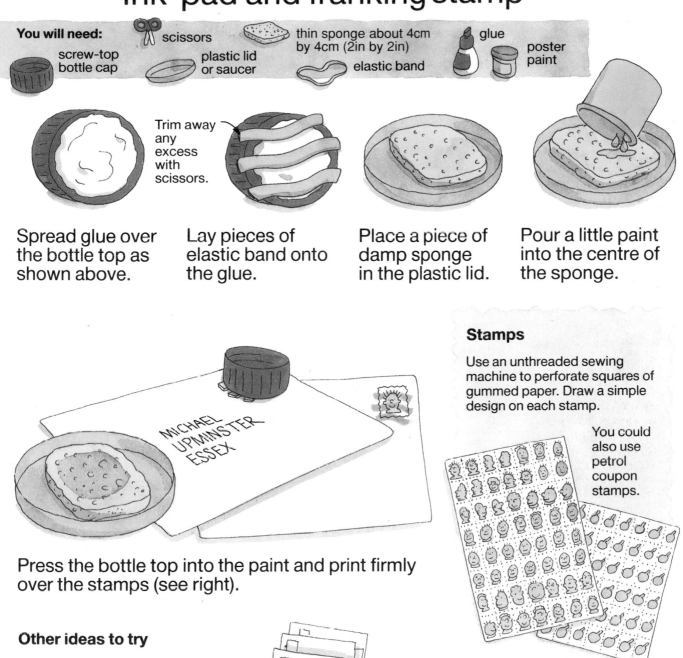

Trim away any excess with scissors.

Spread glue over the bottle top as shown above.

Lay pieces of elastic band onto the glue.

Place a piece of damp sponge in the plastic lid.

Pour a little paint into the centre of the sponge.

MICHAEL UPMINSTER ESSEX

Press the bottle top into the paint and print firmly over the stamps (see right).

Stamps

Use an unthreaded sewing machine to perforate squares of gummed paper. Draw a simple design on each stamp.

You could also use petrol coupon stamps.

Other ideas to try

Counter holder

Cut empty cereal boxes down to different heights. Glue them together in order of size. Stock with postcards, licences and birthday cards to sell.

Add a cardboard tube for holding pens and pencils.

Cash box and money

Use a plastic ice cream box to hold toy money.

Make your own money by cutting notes out of paper.

For coins use washed and flattened foil bottle tops.

Add a toy telephone and some kitchen scales on which to weigh parcels.

Camera and photos

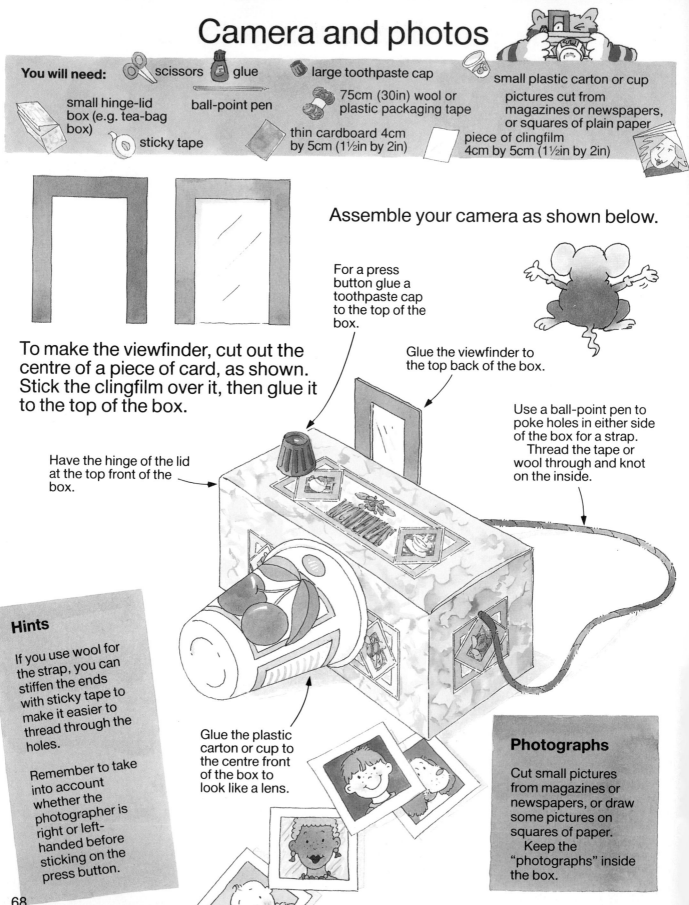

Assemble your camera as shown below.

To make the viewfinder, cut out the centre of a piece of card, as shown. Stick the clingfilm over it, then glue it to the top of the box.

For a press button glue a toothpaste cap to the top of the box.

Glue the viewfinder to the top back of the box.

Use a ball-point pen to poke holes in either side of the box for a strap. Thread the tape or wool through and knot on the inside.

Have the hinge of the lid at the top front of the box.

Hints

If you use wool for the strap, you can stiffen the ends with sticky tape to make it easier to thread through the holes.

Remember to take into account whether the photographer is right or left-handed before sticking on the press button.

Glue the plastic carton or cup to the centre front of the box to look like a lens.

Photographs

Cut small pictures from magazines or newspapers, or draw some pictures on squares of paper.
Keep the "photographs" inside the box.

68

Binoculars

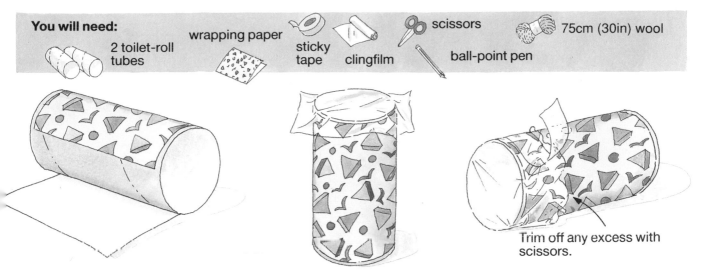

Trim off any excess with scissors.

Cut a piece of wrapping paper to cover each toilet-roll tube. Secure it with sticky tape.

Cut a piece of clingfilm to cover the ends of each toilet-roll tube. Use sticky tape to hold it in place.

Use a ball-point pen to poke two holes for the straps.

Thread wool through the holes. Tie knots in the ends to secure it.

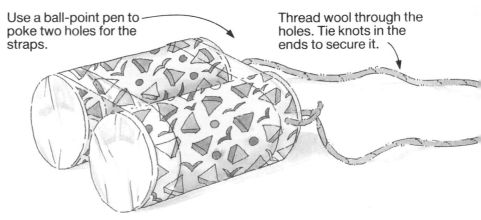

Stick the tubes firmly together using two strips of sticky tape.

Hints

If you have no toilet-roll tubes cut up a kitchen-roll tube using a breadknife as a saw.

When using sticky tape cut the required number of strips and attach them lightly to your work surface ready for use.

Use microwave clingfilm for easier handling.

Other ideas to try

Walkie-talkie

Wrap a 250ml (9fl.oz) juice carton in paper, as you would wrap a small parcel. Use a straw as an aerial.

Stick on squares of gummed paper for buttons and write numbers on them.

Coloured flashlight

Change the colour of a torch beam by securing coloured cellophane over the glass with an elastic band.

Magic telescope

Stick coloured cellophane over a kitchen-roll tube, so that everything looks a different colour.

Moon rocket

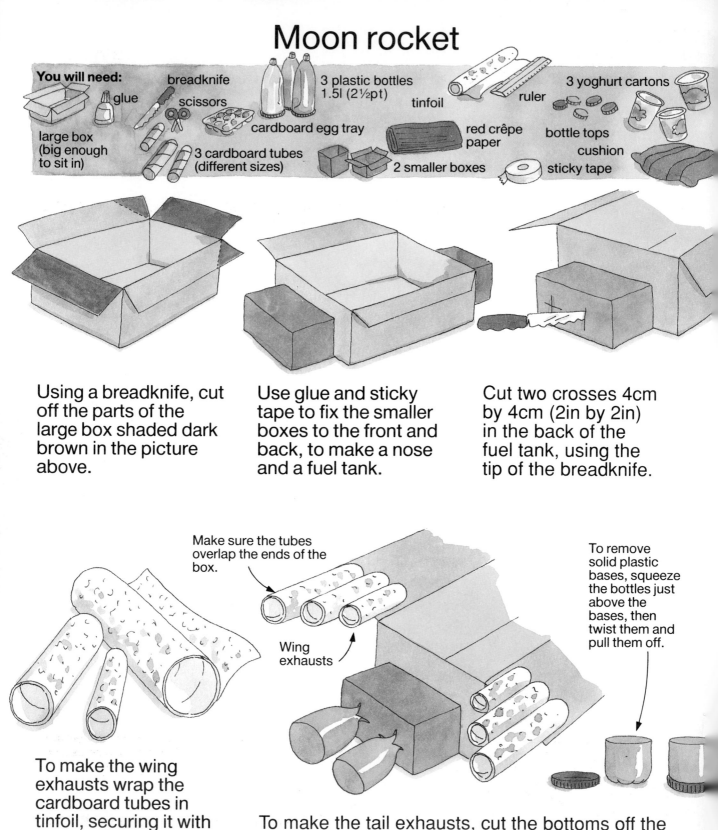

You will need:
glue
breadknife
scissors
large box (big enough to sit in)
3 cardboard tubes (different sizes)
cardboard egg tray
3 plastic bottles 1.5l (2½pt)
tinfoil
2 smaller boxes
ruler
red crêpe paper
sticky tape
3 yoghurt cartons
bottle tops
cushion

Using a breadknife, cut off the parts of the large box shaded dark brown in the picture above.

Use glue and sticky tape to fix the smaller boxes to the front and back, to make a nose and a fuel tank.

Cut two crosses 4cm by 4cm (2in by 2in) in the back of the fuel tank, using the tip of the breadknife.

Make sure the tubes overlap the ends of the box.

Wing exhausts

To remove solid plastic bases, squeeze the bottles just above the bases, then twist them and pull them off.

To make the wing exhausts wrap the cardboard tubes in tinfoil, securing it with sticky tape. Cut each tube in half. Stick the tubes onto the wings.

To make the tail exhausts, cut the bottoms off the bottles about 9cm (3½in) from the base. Insert two of the bottle necks firmly into the crosses cut in the fuel tank. You will need the bases later.

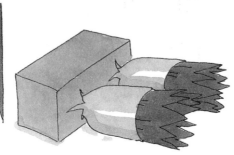

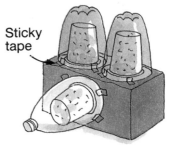

Fold a piece of crêpe paper and cut a jagged edge so that it looks like flames. Cut it into two pieces. Roll each piece loosely and bunch it into the bottles. Secure it with sticky tape.

For lights, cover yoghurt pots with tinfoil. Glue two pots on top of the nose and a third on the front.

Fix the remaining cut bottle and two bottle bases over them with sticky tape.

Sticky tape

Control panel

Cover an egg tray with tinfoil, pressing gently into the hollows.

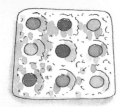

Glue bottle tops in the hollows to make press buttons.

Fix the panel to the inside front of the spaceship.

Add a cushion for the pilot to sit on.

Use an empty washing-liquid container as a can for spare fuel.

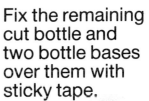

For extra decoration cover the solid plastic bottle bases with toil and stick them onto the wings and fuel tank.

Caravan

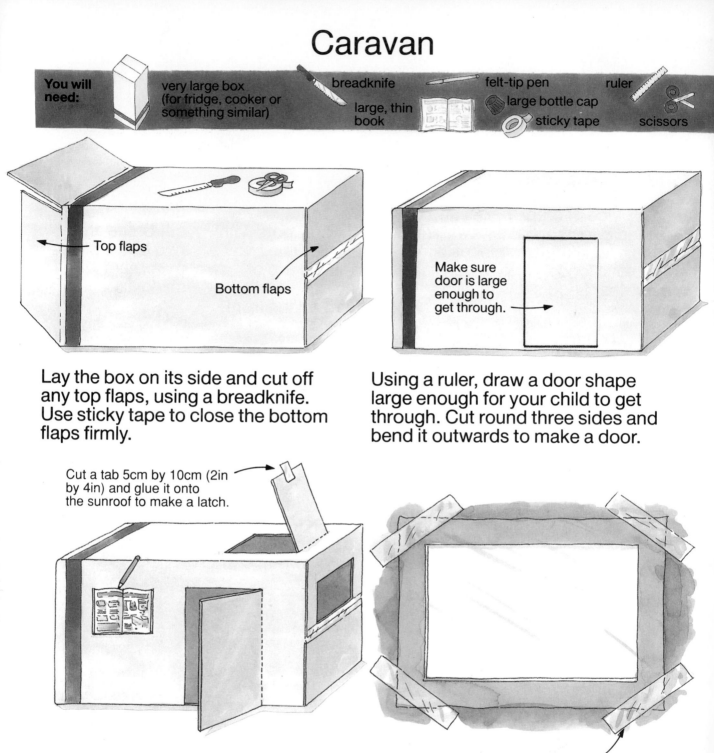

Top flaps

Bottom flaps

Lay the box on its side and cut off any top flaps, using a breadknife. Use sticky tape to close the bottom flaps firmly.

Make sure door is large enough to get through.

Using a ruler, draw a door shape large enough for your child to get through. Cut round three sides and bend it outwards to make a door.

Cut a tab 5cm by 10cm (2in by 4in) and glue it onto the sunroof to make a latch.

Stick tape across the corners first.

To make the windows draw round a thin, open book, then cut round the lines with a breadknife.

Place the book on the roof and draw round it. Cut round three sides and bend the flap up to make a sunroof.

Cut pieces of clingfilm larger than the open book and use sticky tape to fix them over the inside of the windows.

disposable cleaning cloths or remnants of material

glue

clingfilm

4 paper plates or plastic lids

Other ideas to try:

Make a small caravan for a doll or teddy. Choose a box it can fit inside.

Make a tiny caravan from a very small box. Attach it to a toy car, using string or sticky tape.

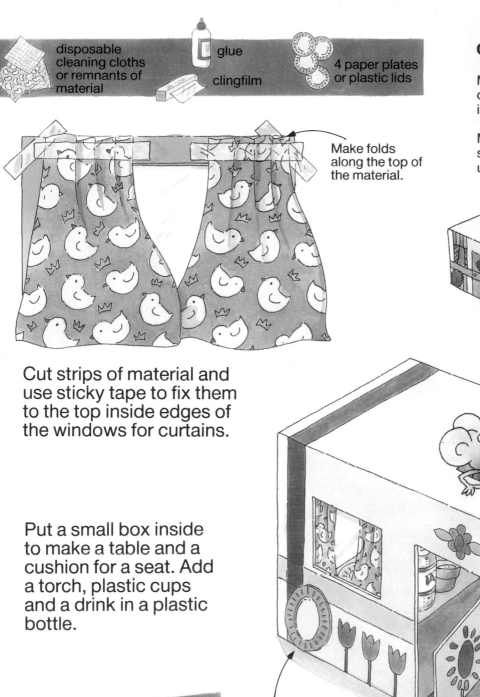

Make folds along the top of the material.

Cut strips of material and use sticky tape to fix them to the top inside edges of the windows for curtains.

Put a small box inside to make a table and a cushion for a seat. Add a torch, plastic cups and a drink in a plastic bottle.

Glue on paper plates for wheels.

Hint

Turn the box so whichever side you are working on is at the top.

You could paint pictures or patterns on your caravan, or make some stripes from coloured sticky tape.

Glue a bottle cap to the door to make a handle.

73

Airport and heliport

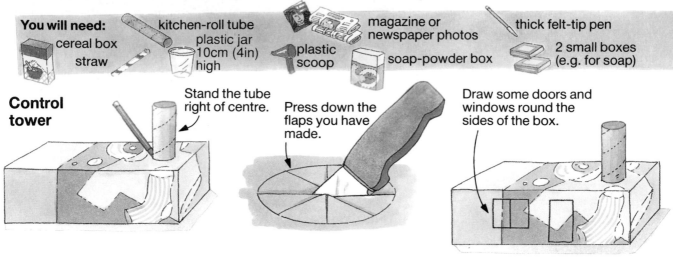

cereal box
straw
kitchen-roll tube
plastic jar
10cm (4in) high
plastic scoop
magazine or newspaper photos
soap-powder box
thick felt-tip pen
2 small boxes (e.g. for soap)

Control tower

Stand the tube right of centre.

Press down the flaps you have made.

Draw some doors and windows round the sides of the box.

Stand the kitchen-roll tube on the soap-powder box, as shown, and draw round it with a felt-tip pen.

Poke a slit in the centre of the circle. Cut to the edge, using a breadknife. Make cuts all the way round, as shown.

Push the kitchen roll firmly into the hole so that it stands upright.

If you have not got a plastic jar, use a breadknife to cut down a clear, plastic bottle.

Helicopter pad

Cut some pictures of people from magazine photographs. Glue them onto the inside of the upturned plastic jar.

Put plenty of glue round the top of the kitchen-roll tube. Press the plastic jar firmly on top.

Remove the lid from a pizza box and turn the box upside down.
Draw round a jar lid to make a large circle in the centre. Write a large "H" for helicopter in the circle.

pizza box · tinfoil · scissors · paper · large jar lid · breadknife · glue

Passenger lounge

Saw a cereal box in half lengthways, using a breadknife. Turn one half on its side and glue it onto the left of the control tower base.

Stick a small box on top of it to make a look-out point. Make a hole in the small box, push in a straw and stick on a paper flag.

Car park

Remove the flaps from the pizza box lid. Draw car spaces on the lid and put it in front of the control tower.

Radar

Push the handle of a scoop into a small box and glue the box to the top of the control tower building.

Runway

Using scissors, cut away the side panel from the remaining half of the cereal box. Open out the box to make a flat strip.

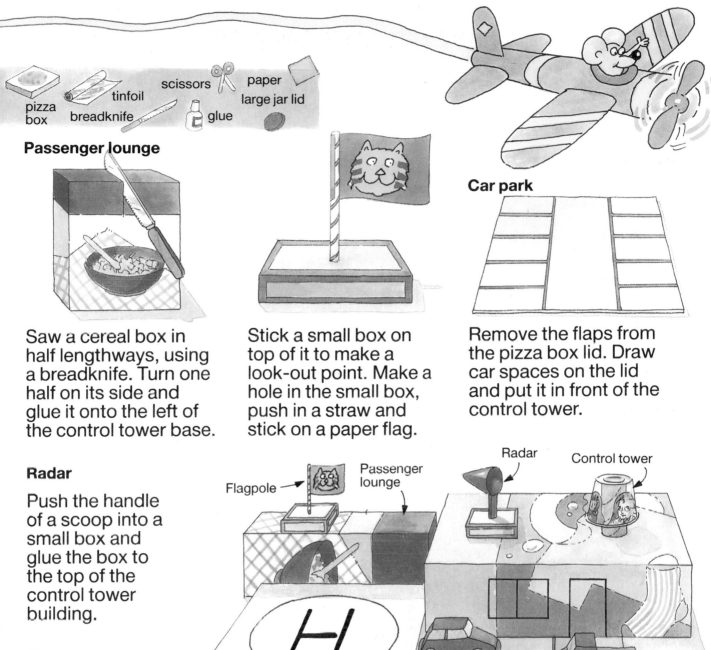

Flagpole
Passenger lounge
Radar
Control tower
Helicopter pad
Car park
Runway

Screw up some pieces of tinfoil and stick them down the edges of the runway for lights.

Use your own toy aeroplanes and cars, plastic figures and traffic signs.

Draw in some centre markings using felt-tip pen.

Pull-along train

You will need: long box with low sides approx. 15cm (6in) high (box 1) · 2 smaller boxes, narrower than box 1 (boxes 2 and 3) · even smaller box (box 4) · fat cardboard tube · plastic tub · toilet-roll tube · sticky tape · glue · ruler · breadknife · ball-point pen

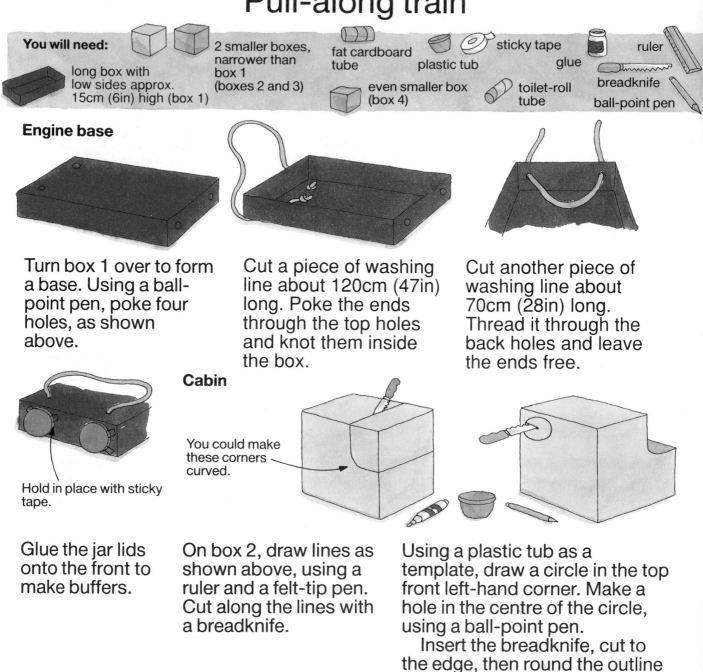

Engine base

Turn box 1 over to form a base. Using a ball-point pen, poke four holes, as shown above.

Cut a piece of washing line about 120cm (47in) long. Poke the ends through the top holes and knot them inside the box.

Cut another piece of washing line about 70cm (28in) long. Thread it through the back holes and leave the ends free.

Glue the jar lids onto the front to make buffers.

Hold in place with sticky tape.

Cabin

You could make these corners curved.

On box 2, draw lines as shown above, using a ruler and a felt-tip pen. Cut along the lines with a breadknife.

Using a plastic tub as a template, draw a circle in the top front left-hand corner. Make a hole in the centre of the circle, using a ball-point pen.

Insert the breadknife, cut to the edge, then round the outline of the circle. Remove the circle to make a window for the driver.

Glue the cabin to the back end of the base. Use sticky tape for extra strength.

76

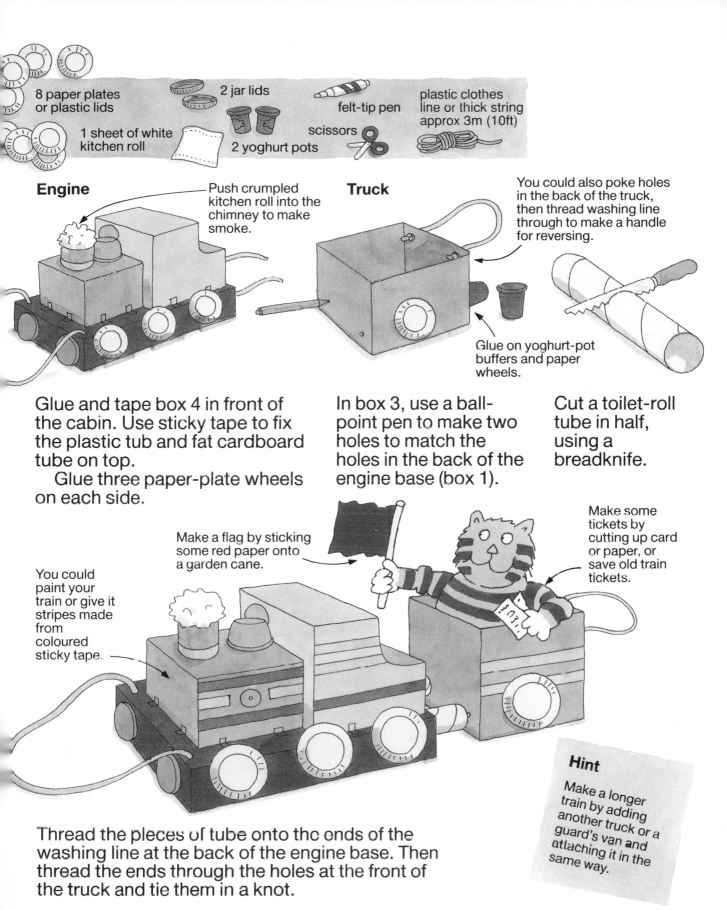

8 paper plates or plastic lids

2 jar lids

felt-tip pen

plastic clothes line or thick string approx 3m (10ft)

1 sheet of white kitchen roll

scissors

2 yoghurt pots

Engine

Push crumpled kitchen roll into the chimney to make smoke.

Truck

You could also poke holes in the back of the truck, then thread washing line through to make a handle for reversing.

Glue on yoghurt-pot buffers and paper wheels.

Glue and tape box 4 in front of the cabin. Use sticky tape to fix the plastic tub and fat cardboard tube on top.

Glue three paper-plate wheels on each side.

In box 3, use a ball-point pen to make two holes to match the holes in the back of the engine base (box 1).

Cut a toilet-roll tube in half, using a breadknife.

Make a flag by sticking some red paper onto a garden cane.

Make some tickets by cutting up card or paper, or save old train tickets.

You could paint your train or give it stripes made from coloured sticky tape.

Thread the pieces of tube onto the ends of the washing line at the back of the engine base. Then thread the ends through the holes at the front of the truck and tie them in a knot.

Hint

Make a longer train by adding another truck or a guard's van and attaching it in the same way.

Dog kennel

You will need: ruler — ball-point pen — sticky tape — scissors — newspaper — flap-top box — breadknife — saucer — felt-tip pen — powder paint — corrugated cardboard — paintbrush

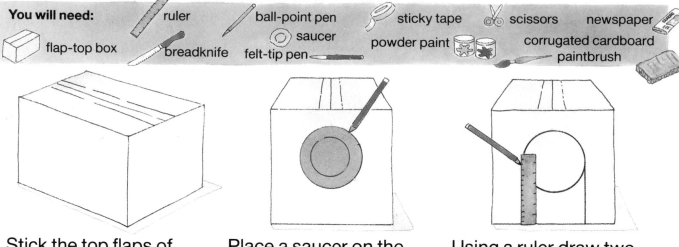

Stick the top flaps of the box down with tape. If necessary, do the same with the bottom flaps.

Place a saucer on the centre front of the box and draw round it with a felt-tip pen.

Using a ruler draw two lines from the sides of the circle to the bottom edge of the box.

Using a breadknife cut round the arch-shape to make a doorway. To insert the knife, first make a hole with a ball-point pen.

Place the box on an old newspaper to paint it.

Write your toy dog's name over the door.

You could decorate a strip of card and stick it round his neck for a collar.

Cut some dog biscuits from corrugated cardboard. You could serve them in a plastic dish.

BONZO

Try putting some old material inside the kennel for a bed.

Another idea to try
Cat basket

Using a ruler, draw a line around a box about 10cm (4in) from the base. Cut off the top using a breadknife.

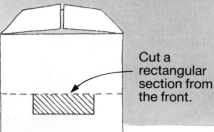

Cut a rectangular section from the front.

Paint the outside of the box and put a cushion inside for your toy cat to sit on.

Tying and threading trays

You will need: polystyrene food trays and pizza bases, sharp pencil, paints, paintbrush, felt-tip pens, bootlaces in a selection of colours

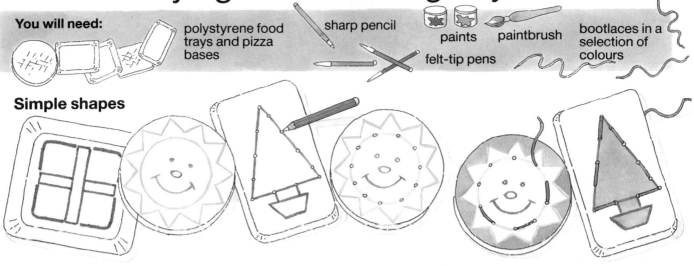

Simple shapes

Draw some large, simple shapes on the back of food trays, using felt-tip pens. You will need to press firmly.

Poke holes at intervals around the main outline, using a pencil with a sharp point.

Paint the shapes. Thread round the outline with laces.

Random patterns

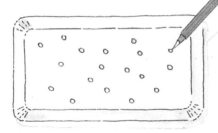

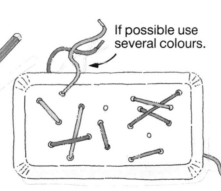

If possible use several colours.

Use a sharp pencil to poke holes through a food tray from the back.

Use the tray for threading criss-cross patterns with bootlaces.

Shoe-laces

Draw and paint a shoe. Poke lace-holes in it.

Use the shoe to practise tying knots and bows.

Other ideas to try

Sewing on buttons

Use scissors to cut the bases off two clean, dry polystyrene cups about 1cm (½in) from the bottom.

Poke two holes in each, using a sharp pencil.

Draw and colour a clown on a food tray or a piece of card. Place the buttons on him and make four holes in the tray or card to correspond with the button holes.

"Sew" on the buttons with bootlaces.

Fleet of boats

You will need: glue • rubber tap washers • flip-open screw cap • coloured tape • sticky tape • paper from glossy magazine • press-down dispenser from bottle • straws • breadknife • string or wool • an assortment of boxes and cartons • brass paper fasteners • margarine tub with lid • scissors

Police launch

Cut a clean dry milk carton in half lengthways.

Cut down a light-bulb box and tape it into the centre of one half of the milk carton.

Radar made from straws. Poke a hole in the box and insert the upright. Tape cross-pieces on with sticky tape.

Flag cut from a magazine.

Searchlights made from brass paper fasteners. Press the heads flat. Push the points a little way into the box and open them out inside.

Rubber tap washers glued onto the sides for lifebelts.

Flagpole made from a straw taped inside the back of the boat.

Tugboat

Trim the bows slightly with scissors.

Glue a flat box (e.g. a sardine box) onto the base of a polystyrene food tray.

Square box (e.g. cut-down light-bulb box) taped or glued on.

Press-down dispenser from liquid-soap bottle. Cut off any tubing and discard. Fix to top of box with sticky tape.

Flip-open screw cap taped on to make a funnel.

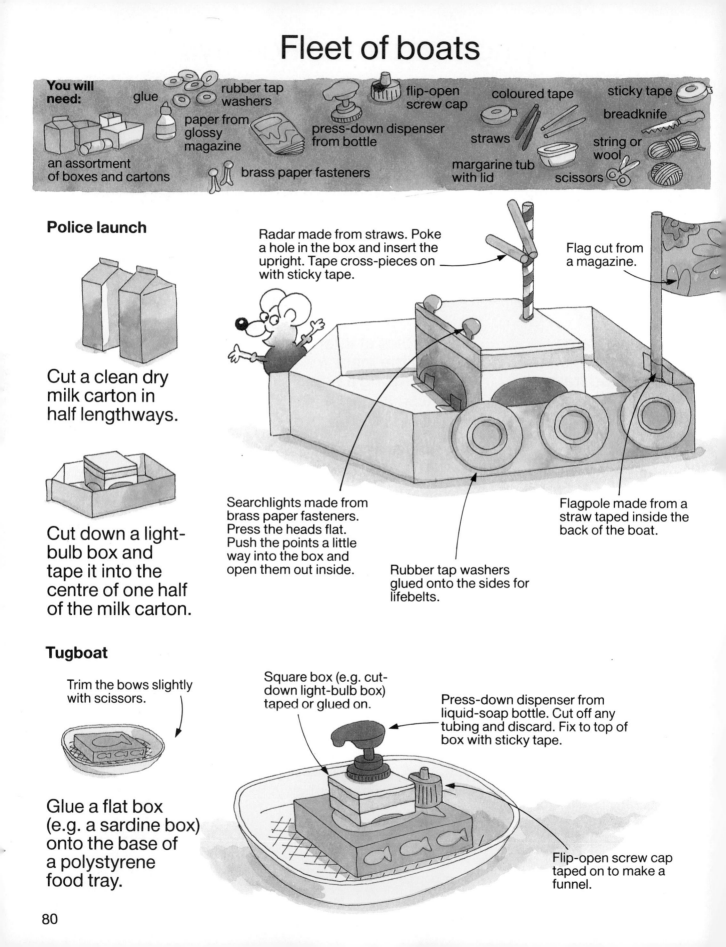

80

Other ideas to try

Hovercraft

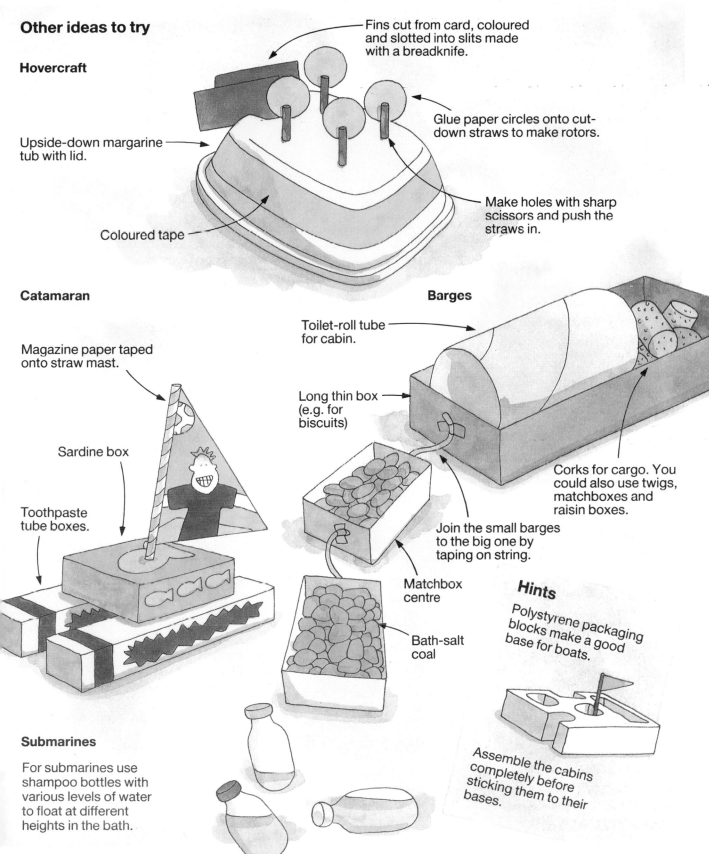

Fins cut from card, coloured and slotted into slits made with a breadknife.

Glue paper circles onto cut-down straws to make rotors.

Upside-down margarine tub with lid.

Make holes with sharp scissors and push the straws in.

Coloured tape

Catamaran

Magazine paper taped onto straw mast.

Sardine box

Toothpaste tube boxes.

Barges

Toilet-roll tube for cabin.

Long thin box (e.g. for biscuits)

Corks for cargo. You could also use twigs, matchboxes and raisin boxes.

Join the small barges to the big one by taping on string.

Matchbox centre

Bath-salt coal

Hints

Polystyrene packaging blocks make a good base for boats.

Assemble the cabins completely before sticking them to their bases.

Submarines

For submarines use shampoo bottles with various levels of water to float at different heights in the bath.

Cooker

You will need: large box · breadknife · ruler · tinfoil · large screw-top bottle cap · 4 plastic tub or jar lids · glue · 5 small bottle caps · sticky tape · scissors · felt-tip pen

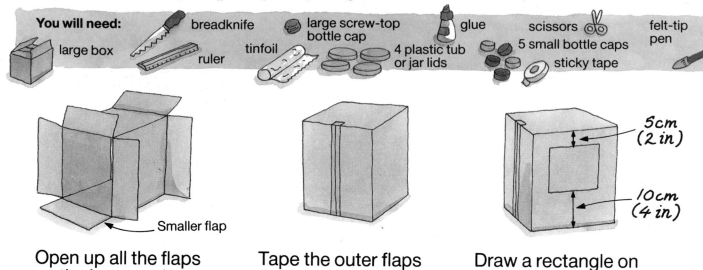

Smaller flap

Open up all the flaps on the box, as shown. Cut off the smaller, inside flaps, using a breadknife.

Tape the outer flaps firmly together at the top and the bottom.

Draw a rectangle on the centre front of the box to make a door.

5cm (2 in)

10cm (4 in)

Using a breadknife, cut round three sides of the rectangle.

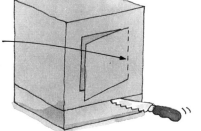

Fold back to make a hinge down the fourth side.

Using the breadknife, cut off the bottom 5cm (2in) of the box.

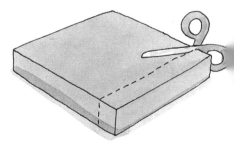

Turn this bottom piece upside down and trim a 1cm (½in) strip from the front.

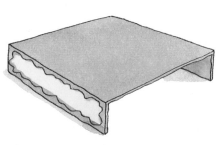

Put glue on the three sides that are left.

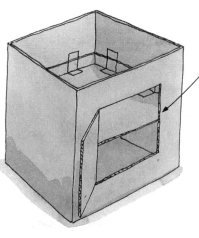

Make sure the trimmed edge of the shelf is at the front.

Turn the cooker upside down and push the glued piece firmly inside to form a shelf halfway down.
   Add sticky tape for extra support.

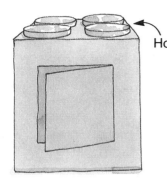

Hot plates

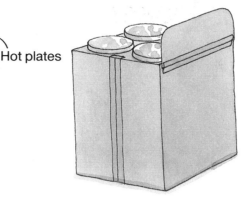

Cover jar lids with pieces of tinfoil and tape them to the top of the cooker.

Cut a strip of card 8cm (3in) deep, round off the top corners and tape it to the back of the cooker.

Other ideas to try

Fridge

Make as for the cooker, but leave out the hot plates and control knobs.

Fill with: egg boxes

empty, washed-out milk cartons

playdough butter and cheese on paper plates or jar lids

crumpled tinfoil fish

margarine and yoghurt tubs

Washing machine

Draw around a circular 1 litre (1¾ pint) ice cream tub on the centre front of a large box. Use a breadknife to cut almost round the circle, but leave a hinge at the side. Glue and tape the lid of the tub onto the door.

Cut a flap on top for soap powder.

Add a large screw-on bottle cap as the programming dial.

To go with your cooker:

Use plastic margarine tubs as pans or mixing bowls.

Draw on a clock face.

Make food from playdough using a rolling pin and plastic cutters.

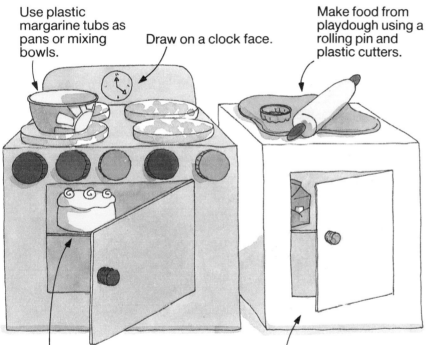

Use playdough to ice an upside-down margarine-tub cake on a paper plate. Add pasta shells as decoration.

Fridge. (See Other ideas to try, on the right.)

Borrow an apron and oven gloves from the kitchen.

Cut out some cardboard biscuits.

Use ice cream tub lids as baking trays.

Glue and tape on bottle-cap knobs. Glue and tape on a screw-top door handle.

Teddy bear's bed

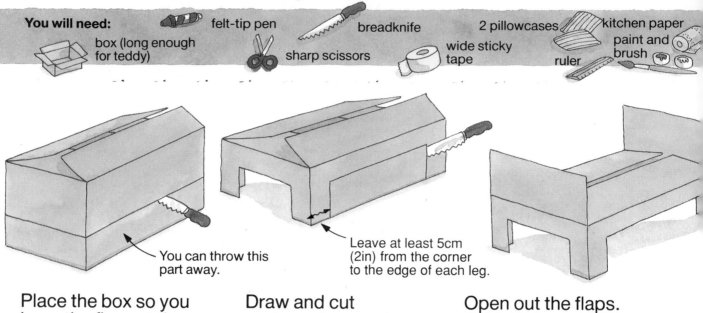

You will need: felt-tip pen · box (long enough for teddy) · sharp scissors · breadknife · wide sticky tape · 2 pillowcases · ruler · kitchen paper · paint and brush

You can throw this part away.

Leave at least 5cm (2in) from the corner to the edge of each leg.

Place the box so you have the flaps at the top. Decide how high you want the bed, draw a line round the bottom and cut off the excess with a breadknife.

Draw and cut rectangular panels from each side, to give the bed four sturdy legs.

Open out the flaps. Fold the longest flaps back into place, leaving the end flaps free.

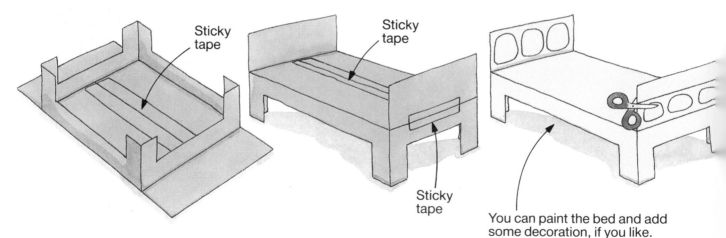

Sticky tape

Sticky tape

Sticky tape

You can paint the bed and add some decoration, if you like.

Turn the bed over and tape the long flaps securely into place underneath.

Turn it upright again and stick tape down the centre, and at each end to hold the end flaps upright.

Cut down one end flap to about two thirds of the height of the other and then round off the corners.

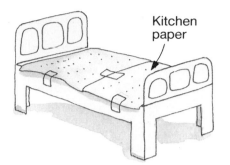

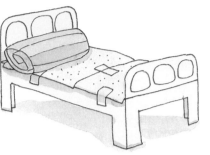

Use pieces of kitchen paper lightly taped onto the bed for a bottom sheet.

For the pillow, fold a pillowcase so that it fits the head end of the bed.

Use a second pillowcase as a blanket. Turn back the top.

Kitchen paper

Other idea to try

Hospital

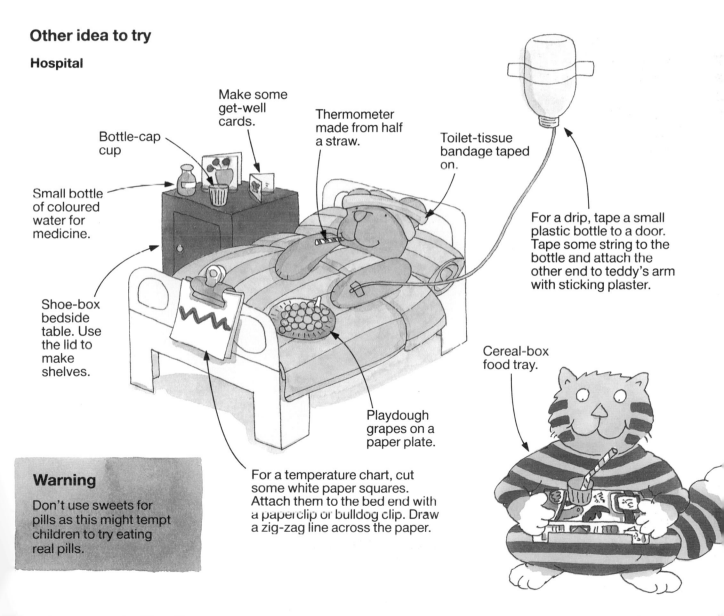

Make some get-well cards.

Thermometer made from half a straw.

Toilet-tissue bandage taped on.

Bottle-cap cup

Small bottle of coloured water for medicine.

For a drip, tape a small plastic bottle to a door. Tape some string to the bottle and attach the other end to teddy's arm with sticking plaster.

Shoe-box bedside table. Use the lid to make shelves.

Cereal-box food tray.

Playdough grapes on a paper plate.

Warning

Don't use sweets for pills as this might tempt children to try eating real pills.

For a temperature chart, cut some white paper squares. Attach them to the bed end with a paperclip or bulldog clip. Draw a zig-zag line across the paper.

Doll's playhouse

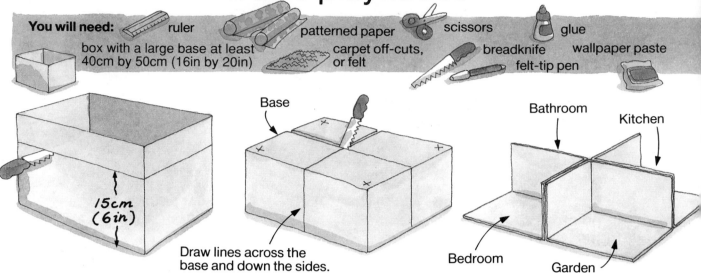

You will need: ruler patterned paper scissors glue
box with a large base at least 40cm by 50cm (16in by 20in) carpet off-cuts, or felt breadknife wallpaper paste
felt-tip pen

15cm (6in)

Base

Draw lines across the base and down the sides.

Bathroom
Kitchen
Bedroom
Garden

Using a ruler and a felt-tip, measure and mark a line all the way round the box, at least 15cm (6in) up from the base. Cut around the line with a breadknife.

Turn the box over and mark each corner with a cross. Measure and mark the box into quarters. Cut the box into four sections with a breadknife.

Keep the sections separate to decorate them. Then fit them together with the crosses in the centre underneath, long sides against long sides.

To paper your rooms

To carpet your rooms

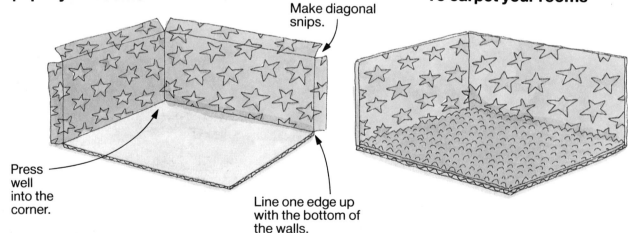

Make diagonal snips.

Press well into the corner.

Line one edge up with the bottom of the walls.

Cut a piece of paper longer and wider than the two walls of your room. Cover the back of the paper with wallpaper paste and stick it to the walls.

Make snips at the edges as shown. Fold the overlaps over and stick them down to make neat edges.

Trim carpet off-cuts or bits of felt, or patterned paper, to the right size. Stick them down with glue.

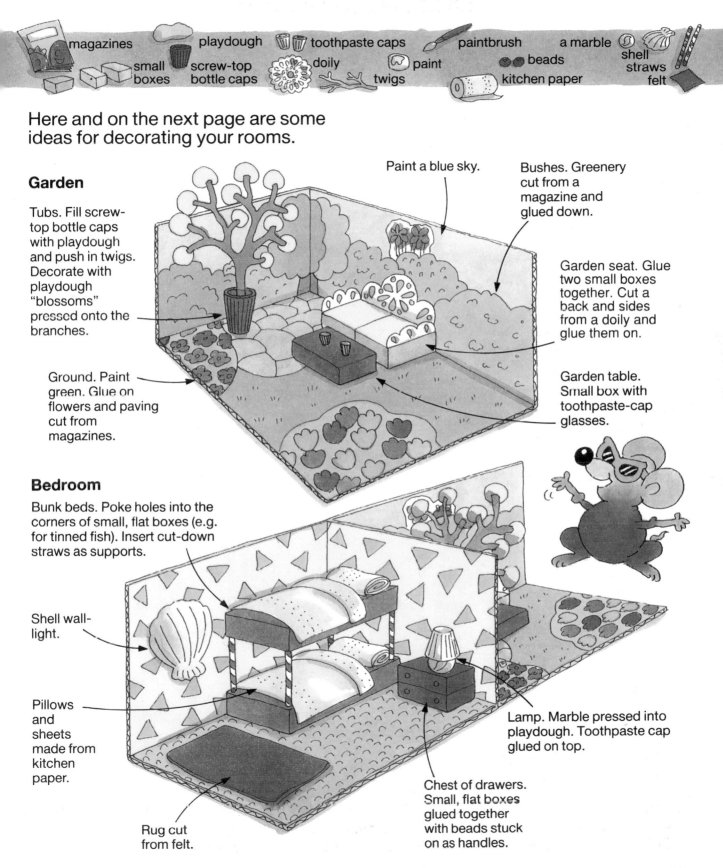

magazines playdough toothpaste caps paintbrush a marble shell
small boxes screw-top bottle caps doily paint beads straws
twigs kitchen paper felt

Here and on the next page are some ideas for decorating your rooms.

Garden

Tubs. Fill screw-top bottle caps with playdough and push in twigs. Decorate with playdough "blossoms" pressed onto the branches.

Ground. Paint green. Glue on flowers and paving cut from magazines.

Paint a blue sky.

Bushes. Greenery cut from a magazine and glued down.

Garden seat. Glue two small boxes together. Cut a back and sides from a doily and glue them on.

Garden table. Small box with toothpaste-cap glasses.

Bedroom

Bunk beds. Poke holes into the corners of small, flat boxes (e.g. for tinned fish). Insert cut-down straws as supports.

Shell wall-light.

Pillows and sheets made from kitchen paper.

Rug cut from felt.

Lamp. Marble pressed into playdough. Toothpaste cap glued on top.

Chest of drawers. Small, flat boxes glued together with beads stuck on as handles.

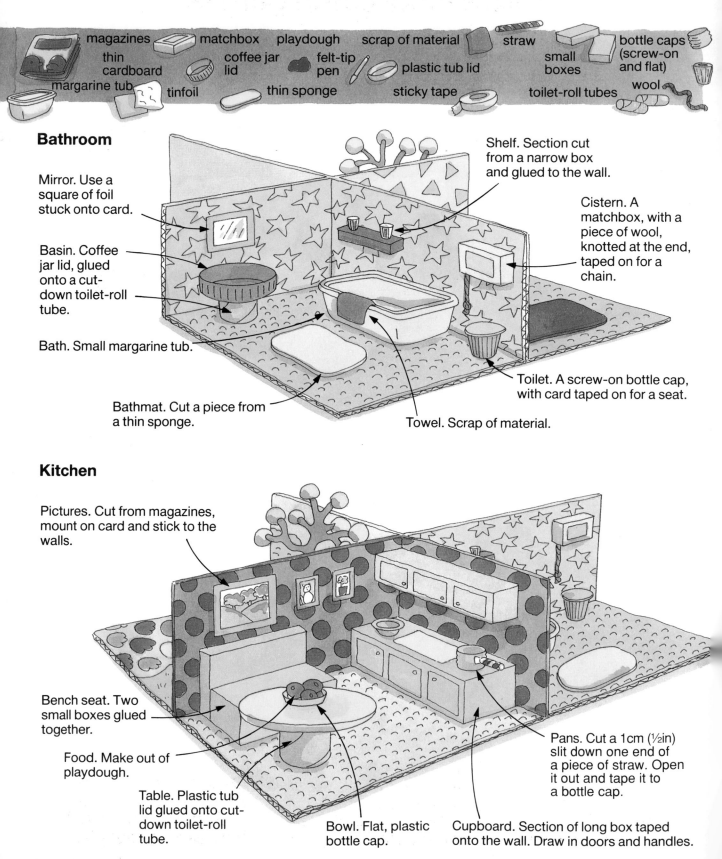

magazines matchbox playdough scrap of material straw bottle caps (screw-on and flat)
thin cardboard coffee jar lid felt-tip pen plastic tub lid small boxes
margarine tub tinfoil thin sponge sticky tape toilet-roll tubes wool

Bathroom

Mirror. Use a square of foil stuck onto card.

Basin. Coffee jar lid, glued onto a cut-down toilet-roll tube.

Bath. Small margarine tub.

Bathmat. Cut a piece from a thin sponge.

Shelf. Section cut from a narrow box and glued to the wall.

Cistern. A matchbox, with a piece of wool, knotted at the end, taped on for a chain.

Toilet. A screw-on bottle cap, with card taped on for a seat.

Towel. Scrap of material.

Kitchen

Pictures. Cut from magazines, mount on card and stick to the walls.

Bench seat. Two small boxes glued together.

Food. Make out of playdough.

Table. Plastic tub lid glued onto cut-down toilet-roll tube.

Bowl. Flat, plastic bottle cap.

Pans. Cut a 1cm (½in) slit down one end of a piece of straw. Open it out and tape it to a bottle cap.

Cupboard. Section of long box taped onto the wall. Draw in doors and handles.

88

Throw-and-catch games

You will need: sticky tape · large plastic bottles · scissors · breadknife · paper or piece of real sponge · string or wool 30cm (1ft)

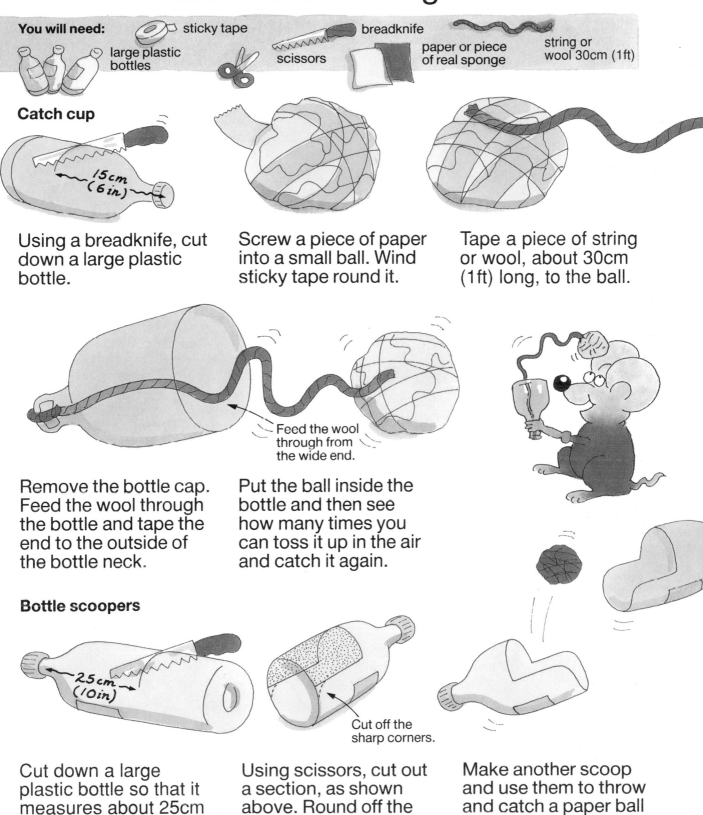

Catch cup

15cm (6in)

Using a breadknife, cut down a large plastic bottle.

Screw a piece of paper into a small ball. Wind sticky tape round it.

Tape a piece of string or wool, about 30cm (1ft) long, to the ball.

Feed the wool through from the wide end.

Remove the bottle cap. Feed the wool through the bottle and tape the end to the outside of the bottle neck.

Put the ball inside the bottle and then see how many times you can toss it up in the air and catch it again.

Bottle scoopers

25cm (10in)

Cut off the sharp corners.

Cut down a large plastic bottle so that it measures about 25cm (10in) from the neck.

Using scissors, cut out a section, as shown above. Round off the corners for safety.

Make another scoop and use them to throw and catch a paper ball between two people.

89

Guessing box

You will need: food tin (unopened) · kitchen cloth or other light material · felt-tip pen · scissors · shoe box · ruler · sticky tape · breadknife · various small objects

Cut a rectangle out of one of the small sides of a shoe box.

Put a tin in the middle of the opposite end. Draw round it, using a felt-tip pen.

Push the point of a breadknife into the centre of the circle. Cut outwards to the edge and then round the circle.

Make sure you can fit your hand inside.

Using the tin as a guide, cut a rectangle of material big enough to cover the circle easily. Cut it in half up the centre.

Cut up here.

Tape along the top and down the sides.

Tape the material to the inside of the box so that it covers the hole. Replace the box lid.

How to play

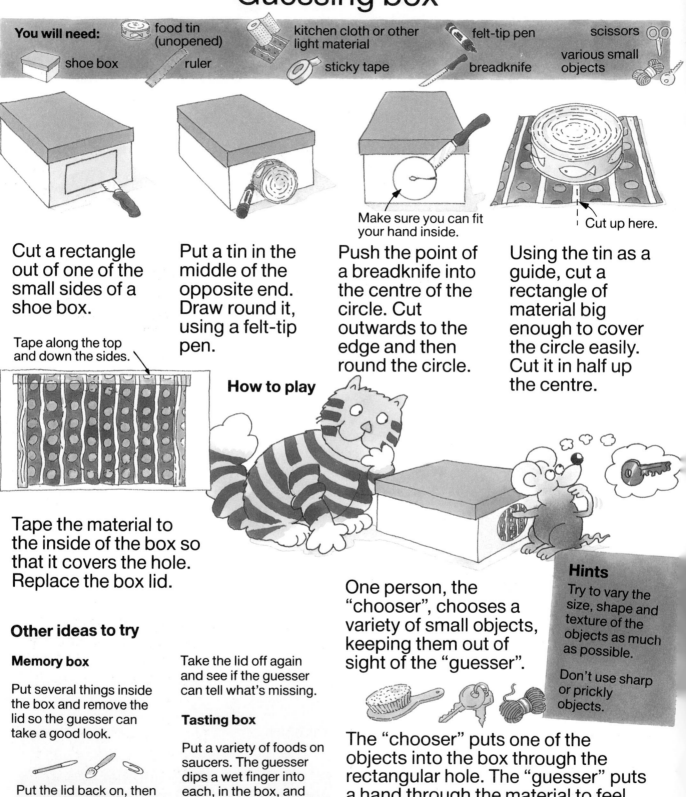

One person, the "chooser", chooses a variety of small objects, keeping them out of sight of the "guesser".

The "chooser" puts one of the objects into the box through the rectangular hole. The "guesser" puts a hand through the material to feel the mystery object and tries to guess what it is.

Hints

Try to vary the size, shape and texture of the objects as much as possible.

Don't use sharp or prickly objects.

Other ideas to try

Memory box

Put several things inside the box and remove the lid so the guesser can take a good look.

Put the lid back on, then remove one object without the guesser seeing.

Take the lid off again and see if the guesser can tell what's missing.

Tasting box

Put a variety of foods on saucers. The guesser dips a wet finger into each, in the box, and tastes it with their eyes closed.

Blow football

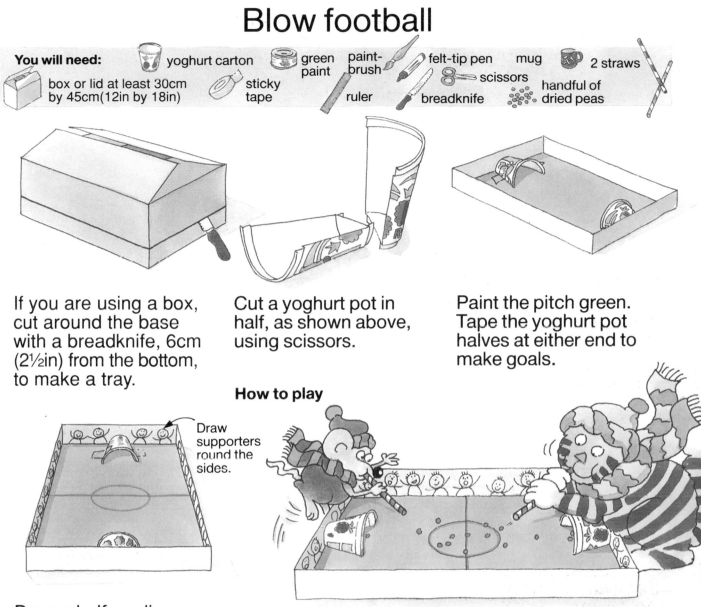

If you are using a box, cut around the base with a breadknife, 6cm (2½in) from the bottom, to make a tray.

Cut a yoghurt pot in half, as shown above, using scissors.

Paint the pitch green. Tape the yoghurt pot halves at either end to make goals.

How to play

Draw supporters round the sides.

Draw a halfway line using a ruler and felt-tip pen. Draw round a mug to make a centre circle.

Put a handful of dried peas into the centre circle.

Each player has a straw and uses it to try to blow as many peas as possible into the opposite goal.

The game is over when all the peas are in goal. Count them to find out who is the winner.

Another idea to try

Throw ball

Mark a line on the floor with a piece of wool. Throw screwed-up paper balls into a propped-up box from behind the line.

Nodding elephant

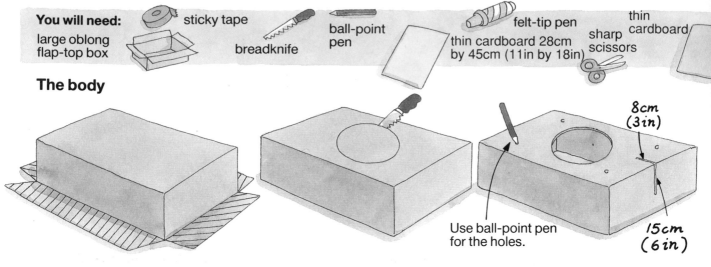

You will need: sticky tape, large oblong flap-top box, breadknife, ball-point pen, felt-tip pen, thin cardboard 28cm by 45cm (11in by 18in), sharp scissors, thin cardboard

The body

8cm (3in)

15cm (6in)

Use ball-point pen for the holes.

Turn the box over and cut off the flaps with a breadknife.

Cut a circle in the centre top, large enough to fit round your child's waist.

Cut a slit along the top and down the front, as shown. Poke four holes in the top for straps.

The head

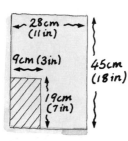

28cm (11in)
9cm (3in)
45cm (18in)
19cm (7in)

Cut out this part.

Cut a rectangle 9cm by 19cm (3in by 7½in) from the corner of a large piece of card.

Round off the corners with scissors. Draw in a trunk and cut it out.

Draw round the end of a kitchen-roll tube to make two circles, as shown above.

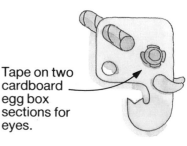

Tape on two cardboard egg box sections for eyes.

Cut slits from the centres to very slightly beyond the edges.

Push the kitchen-roll tube through the top hole to make handles.

Cut two tusks out of the cardboard-box flaps and glue them onto the head.

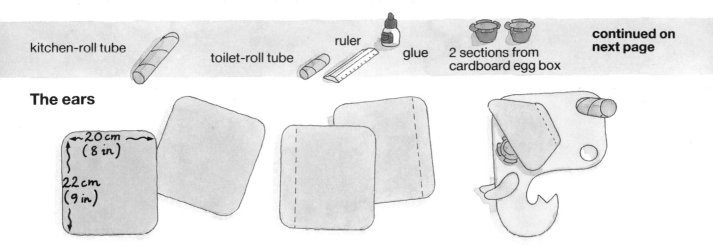

kitchen-roll tube

toilet-roll tube

ruler

glue

2 sections from cardboard egg box

continued on next page

The ears

←20cm→
(8 in)

22 cm
(9 in)

Cut two rectangles out of card. Round off the corners, using scissors.

Make a fold down one long side of each rectangle, 4cm (1½in) from the edge.

Put some glue along the folds and stick the ears onto each side of the head between the eye and the handle.

Joining the head and body

Add sticky tape for extra strength.

Hint

Make sure the hole is big enough for the tube before you fix the head and body together.

Put plenty of glue on either side of the front slit of the body box, on the inside of the box.
　Push the head through the slit from the outside, so that the hole in the head is on the inside.

Stand the box on end while you fix the head.

Push a toilet-roll tube through the hole and press it firmly against the glued area.

93

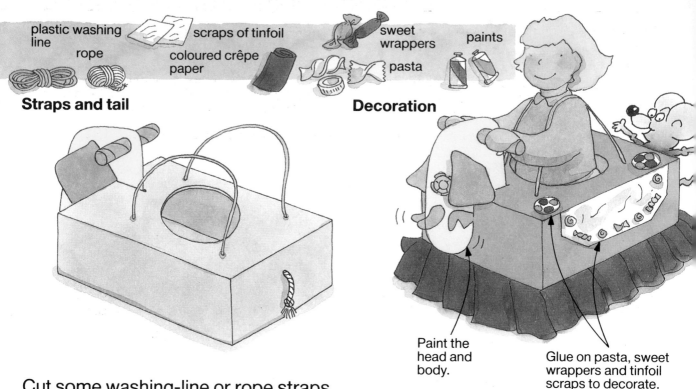

plastic washing line

rope

scraps of tinfoil

coloured crêpe paper

sweet wrappers

pasta

paints

Straps and tail

Decoration

Paint the head and body.

Glue on pasta, sweet wrappers and tinfoil scraps to decorate.

Cut some washing-line or rope straps the right length to fit over the wearer's shoulders. Thread them through the holes and knot them inside.

Make a hole for a tail with a ball-point pen. Thread some rope through and knot it inside. Knot and fray the end.

Cut a strip of crêpe paper about 20cm (8in) wide to go around the lower edge of the elephant's body. Attach it with sticky tape. Stretch the lower edge between your hands to make a frilled effect.

Other ideas to try

Clown horse

Crêpe-paper mane

Slit crêpe-paper fringe

Dinosaur

Spines cut from crêpe-paper.

Duck

Paper wings and tail

Yellow socks

On this page and the following one you will find some general advice about the equipment and materials needed for the projects in this book, and ways of handling them. The specific things you will need for each project are listed at the top of each page. It is a good idea to collect them all together before you start work.

Work with your child, explaining each stage of your project as you set about it, referring to the pictures and discussing the materials. The process of making the things is just as important as the end result. There will be parts of some of the projects that are too difficult or dangerous for children to do themselves, but they can still learn a lot from watching and helping you.

Some of the projects towards the end of the book will take a little longer than the earlier ones. You will probably want to do them in two or three sessions, rather than all at once. Explain this to your child before you start.

Basic equipment

For nearly all the projects you will need the following:

- Scissors – for cutting paper and thin cardboard. Round-ended with metal blades for children and, occasionally, sharp-ended for adults only.

- Knife – for cutting thick cardboard. The best type to use is a breadknife or other sturdy knife with a serrated edge. For adults only.

- Felt-tip pen – for marking lines to cut along.

- Ball-point pen – for making holes in cardboard.

- Ruler – for measuring.

- Pencil

- Glue

- Sticky tape

Finding your materials

You can collect nearly all of the materials you will need by saving the packaging from your everyday shopping. The lists below will help you to spot the sort of things that will come in handy.

Cardboard boxes and cartons for:

Cereal (a good source of thin cardboard)

tea bags and loose tea

soap

soap powder

toothpaste tubes

sardines

eggs

biscuits

matches

shoes

milk and juice

pizzas

Plastic containers for:

shampoos and conditioners

fizzy drinks and squashes

yoghurt

margarine

spreads

ice cream

clothes-washing liquid

dishwashing liquid

Polystyrene:

food trays   pizza bases

Lids and caps (metal or plastic) for:

bottles (flat and screw-topped)

jam-jars

toothpaste tubes

margarine and yoghurt tubs

liquid soaps

Cardboard tubes for:

toilet paper   wrapping paper

kitchen roll

Parents' notes

It is also worth saving a few other everyday odds and ends:

Paper:

wrapping paper from flowers or presents

left-over wallpaper

old magazines

sweet wrappers

tissue paper

crêpe paper

Things for tying and threading:

laces

wool

string

rope

plastic washing line

Things from your kitchen

kitchen paper

tinfoil

clingfilm (use microwave clingfilm if possible – it is thicker and less fly-away)

disposable cleaning cloths

thin mopping-up sponges

paper and plastic plates and cups

straws

Asking at shops

Some of the projects require fairly large cardboard boxes. Grocery stores or supermarkets can normally let you have a selection of flap-top boxes. For really large boxes ask at electrical stores that sell fridges, washing machines etc.

Shoe shops usually have some unwanted, empty shoe boxes and sweet shops may be able to give you large, empty, plastic jars.

Cleaning your materials

Wash things like yoghurt pots and bottle caps before using them and wipe paper plates with a damp cloth. Make sure anything you use is thoroughly dry, however, before using glue or sticky tape on it.

It is a good idea to sterilize some things before use e.g. polystyrene food trays, which are porous and may have held meat. Buy a sterilizing solution from a chemist's and follow the instructions. Then, rinse and dry thoroughly before use.

Cutting cardboard

Children who are fairly competent at cutting paper with scissors may be able to cope with cutting thin card, but it is quite tiring on the hand and they will probably need help.

The best way of cutting thick card and large boxes is to use a breadknife as though it were a saw – the downward stroke away from you should have the most pressure. Make it clear to young children that they should not try to do this themselves and keep the knife out of reach. Make sure your child stands well back when you are sawing.

When cutting the top or bottom section off a box, start by sawing across a corner, then insert the blade and continue.

To cut into a flat surface, first insert the point of a ball-point pen to make a small hole for the blade of the knife to fit into.

Turn the box as you cut, so that the area you are cutting is always at the top. This will give you greater control.

Sticking

●Wallpaper paste. This is good for large areas but is not very strong. For safety always use the non-fungicidal kind. You can store left-over paste in the fridge, covered with clingfilm.

●PVA (polyvinyl acetate) glues. These are also good for large areas. They are available from large newsagent's. Apply the glue with a brush. It is white but dries transparent. Protect clothing and wash brushes after use.

●Strong glue. For some jobs, such as sticking yoghurt pots or bottle caps onto cardboard, you need to use a fairly strong glue. Buy a tube of non-toxic glue from a newsagent. Do not use solvent-based or instant-bond glues.

●Coloured sticky tape. This is good for decoration if you want stripes, bars or criss-cross patterns.

Painting

Use powder paints or liquid poster paints. Powder paint is cheaper but tends to be thinner. You can thicken it by mixing it with wallpaper paste, flour and water paste, PVA glue or soapflakes. If you mix a little washing-up liquid into the paint, it will wash off furniture and clothes more easily. For painting large areas, use small adult-sized brushes.

KITCHEN FUN

This book provides parents and children with lots of easy, tasty and original ideas for things to cook together. There are sweets and savouries, including recipes for everyday dishes or for special occasions. Besides introducing children to some of the most basic cooking techniques and giving them fun and satisfaction, the activities in this book will also help to develop their ideas about size, shape, weight, measurement and time, broaden their vocabulary and give them early counting and reading opportunities.

Juicy jellies

Jelly pond

Make up green and yellow jellies together, as directed on the packet, in a large mixing bowl. When cool refrigerate until beginning to set.

Cut pieces of icing off the block and colour them by rolling them in a few drops of food colouring. Leave some white.

Make fish, snakes and snails from the icing (see below). Press them firmly onto the inside of a glass or plastic bowl.

When the jelly is nearly set, pour it carefully into the glass bowl.*

Reeds made from angelica pressed into strips of icing.

When the jelly is firmly set, arrange some ducks, weeds, waterlilies and reeds on the top.

Weeds made from green icing squeezed through a garlic press.

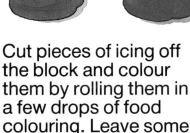

Fish
Flatten a piece of icing. Cut out body and tail shapes. Press in an eye with a pencil covered in clingfilm. Press on some tiny spots.

Snakes
Roll long sausage shapes and press in eyes.

Ducks
Press two balls together, then pinch out a tail and add a beak.

Waterlilies
Flatten balls and shape them into leaves. Mark with a knife. Place flower sweets on top.

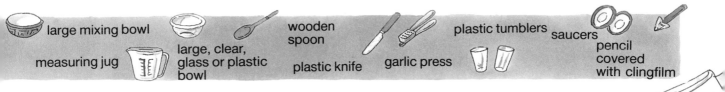

large mixing bowl

large, clear, glass or plastic bowl

measuring jug

wooden spoon

plastic knife

garlic press

plastic tumblers

saucers

pencil covered with clingfilm

Jelly wobblers

Make up a jelly with 75 ml (3fl.oz) less water than given in the instructions. Allow to cool but not set.

Peel, slice and de-seed fresh fruit, or drain canned fruit, and arrange in plastic tumblers.

Pour on the jelly and leave it to set in the fridge.

When they have set, ease round the sides of the jellies with a plastic knife.

Turn them out onto saucers and decorate the tops with cream and fruit.

Other ideas to try:

Monster in a lake
Roll a long, fat snake out of ready roll icing. Cut it into four sections.

Jelly diamond sweets

Bend the middle sections and place them on a set jelly.

Water babies
On a set jelly, arrange some icing "rocks" and stand jelly babies on them.
Add squirty cream for waves.

*Hint
Don't pour liquid jelly over icing or it will start to dissolve.

Fishy puffs

You will need: packet of puff pastry (thawed), 1 egg, lemon, parsley, flour, smoked mackerel or drained can of tuna

Press in lines.

Roll out the puff pastry thinly, about 2mm (1/8in) deep, on a floured surface.

To make large fish cut round a side plate with a knife. For small fish use scone-cutters.

From the leftover pastry cut out tail shapes with a knife. Use a pen-top dipped in flour to cut out "spots".

Fat bunnies

Use scone-cutters to make two circles. Put some filling on one circle and press the other circle over it.

Cut two fat cheeks with a bottle-top. Stick them on.

From another circle cut out two ears.

Roll a small ball for a nose and press out some eyes with a straw. Brush with egg and bake as for fishy puffs.

Leave the edges uncovered.

Place the pastry circle on an oiled baking tray. Brush the edges with beaten egg.

Put some fish on one half of the pastry. Add a squeeze of lemon and some parsley.

Fillings
● Cottage cheese with peas or honey.
● Triangle of processed cheese with a small slice of ham.

rolling pin | plastic knife, fork and spoon | large pen-top | side plate | straw | scone-cutter | bottle-top | fish-slice | pastry brush | oiled baking tray | cooling rack

Fold the circle in half to enclose the fish filling. Press the edge down with a fork.

Use a straw to press out the eye. Press on the tail, using beaten egg to make it stick.

Mark in a mouth and scales with the side of a spoon. Stick on the spots with beaten egg.

Brush all over with beaten egg. Bake in a preheated oven until

puffed and golden (about 15 mins).

Other ideas

Banana puffs ▶
Cut a long strip of pastry. Brush it with egg. Wrap it round half a banana. Brush with egg and bake.

◀ **Little crabs**
Roll triangles of pastry round filling. Curve the ends around. Add eyes. Glaze and bake.

Apple bites
Fold small circles of pastry over a thin slice of apple and brown sugar. Glaze and bake.

Fat parcels
Fold oblongs of pastry over filling. Press down the edges. Add pastry string and stamps. Glaze and bake.

101

Valentine tarts

Set oven to:
200°C   400°F
Gas mark 6

You will need:

- 100g (3½oz) plain or self-raising flour
- pinch of salt
- 25g (1oz) margarine
- 25g (1oz) lard
- jam
- 2 tablespoons cold water
- large mixing bowl
- knife
- plastic scone-cutter
- teaspoon
- plastic bottle-top
- cooling rack
- greased bun tray

Mix the flour and salt in a large bowl. Cut up the fat and gently rub it in.

Stir in the water quickly with a knife.

Push the dough together with your fingers.

Push in top edge, using clingfilm covered pencil.

Pinch lower edge into a point.

Flatten out gently with fingertips.

Roll out the dough on a floured board until it is about 3mm (¼in) thick. Cut out large circles with a scone-cutter.

From the scraps cut out some small circles with a bottle-top and make them into hearts as shown.

Bake for about 15 minutes in a preheated oven.

Press the large circles gently into a greased bun tray. Put a large teaspoon of jam in each one and place the hearts on top.

Hints
- Use a ball of dough to press the circles of pastry gently into the bun tray.
- Do not put too much jam in the tarts, or it may bubble over the edges.
- Allow the jam plenty of time to cool down, before touching or tasting the tarts.

Duck on a lake cake

You will need:

1 quantity Victoria sponge cake mix (see page 128).   pink and green food colouring   jam   icing sugar

1 large bowl   2 dessert spoons   knife   breadknife   thick felt-tip pen   sieve

2 small bowls   greased cake tin approx. 18cm (7in)   scissors   greaseproof paper   cooling rack

Leave one bowl uncoloured.

Make up your cake mixture in a large bowl (see page 128).

Put a third of the mixture into each small bowl. Leave a third in the large bowl.

Add pink food colouring to one bowl and green colouring to another and mix in well.

Put the three parts of the mixture in separate heaps in a cake tin.

Marble it by dragging a spoon gently through the colours.

Bake in the oven for 40 to 45 minutes.

When it is cool slice it in half with a breadknife and spread one half with jam.

To sift the icing sugar tap the sieve gently with the flat of your hand.

You need this part.

Hint
If the greaseproof paper stencil will not lie flat on the cake, brush it with a little water.

Using the cake tin as a guide to size, draw a simple duck design with a felt-tip pen on greaseproof paper. Cut it out carefully to make a stencil.
   Lay the stencil over the cake. Sift icing sugar thickly over it. Lift the paper off carefully.

103

Jelly baby fun

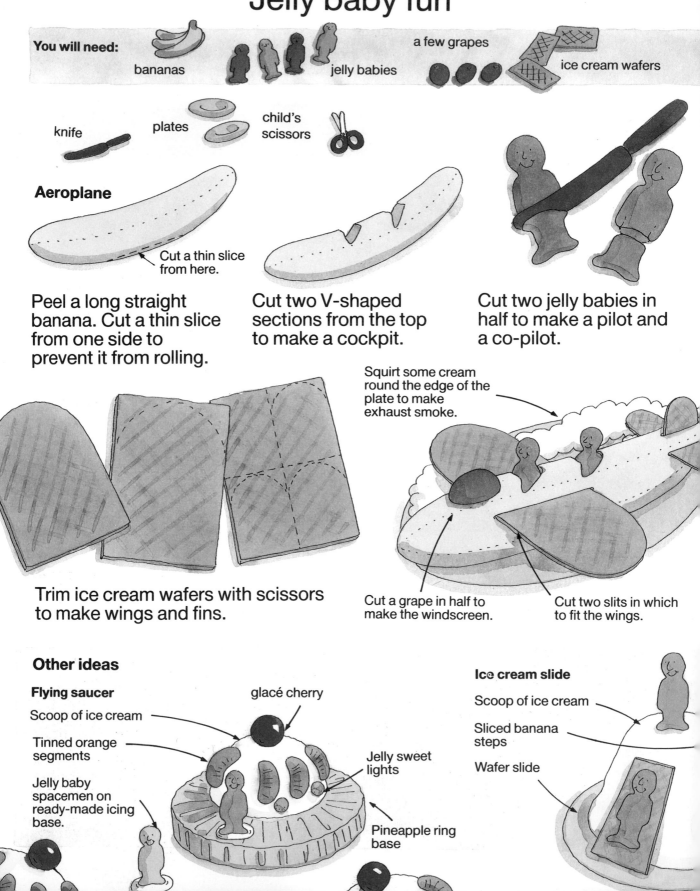

You will need: bananas · jelly babies · a few grapes · ice cream wafers · knife · plates · child's scissors

Aeroplane

Cut a thin slice from here.

Peel a long straight banana. Cut a thin slice from one side to prevent it from rolling.

Cut two V-shaped sections from the top to make a cockpit.

Cut two jelly babies in half to make a pilot and a co-pilot.

Trim ice cream wafers with scissors to make wings and fins.

Squirt some cream round the edge of the plate to make exhaust smoke.

Cut a grape in half to make the windscreen.

Cut two slits in which to fit the wings.

Other ideas

Flying saucer

Scoop of ice cream

Tinned orange segments

Jelly baby spacemen on ready-made icing base.

glacé cherry

Jelly sweet lights

Pineapple ring base

Ice cream slide

Scoop of ice cream

Sliced banana steps

Wafer slide

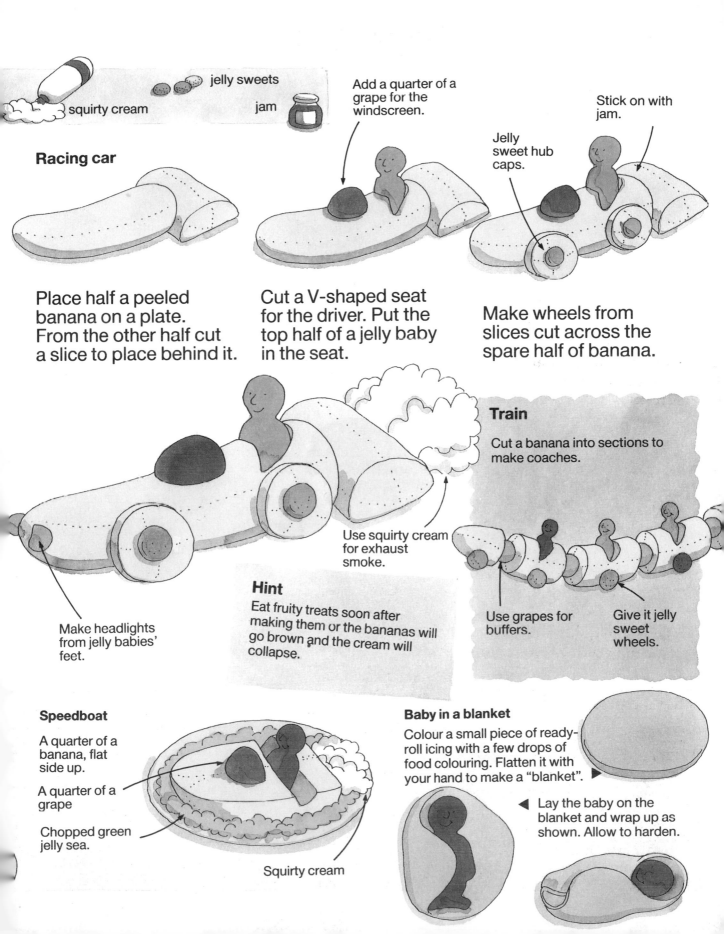

squirty cream

jelly sweets

jam

Racing car

Add a quarter of a grape for the windscreen.

Jelly sweet hub caps.

Stick on with jam.

Place half a peeled banana on a plate. From the other half cut a slice to place behind it.

Cut a V-shaped seat for the driver. Put the top half of a jelly baby in the seat.

Make wheels from slices cut across the spare half of banana.

Use squirty cream for exhaust smoke.

Make headlights from jelly babies' feet.

Train

Cut a banana into sections to make coaches.

Use grapes for buffers.

Give it jelly sweet wheels.

Hint

Eat fruity treats soon after making them or the bananas will go brown and the cream will collapse.

Speedboat

A quarter of a banana, flat side up.

A quarter of a grape

Chopped green jelly sea.

Squirty cream

Baby in a blanket

Colour a small piece of ready-roll icing with a few drops of food colouring. Flatten it with your hand to make a "blanket".

◀ Lay the baby on the blanket and wrap up as shown. Allow to harden.

Flowery hats

You will need:
chocolate or plain round biscuits

packet chocolate teacakes (marshmallow biscuits)

cold water

icing sugar

jelly diamonds

sugar flowers

small bowl
teaspoon
large plate
knife

Make it quite thick so it doesn't run.

Add a little water to icing sugar to make icing "glue".

Spread a little on the centre of each flat biscuit.

Press teacakes gently onto the centre of the biscuits.

Add flowers and jelly diamond "leaves" round the crown. Stick them on with icing glue. Leave to dry.

Add a ready-roll icing "ribbon" if you like.

Other ideas

Christmas puddings

Spread a biscuit with coloured icing to make a plate.

Stick a teacake on.

Dribble a little white icing "brandy sauce" over the top.

Add small pieces of jelly diamonds for leaves and holly berries.

Flying saucers

Ice a biscuit. Add a teacake. Sprinkle hundreds and thousands around the edge. Add jelly sweet lights.

106

Bow-tie bears

You will need:
- 150g (5oz) self-raising flour
- 15g (¾oz) drinking chocolate
- sultanas
- ready-roll icing
- 100g (3½oz) margarine
- 50g (2oz) castor sugar
- ½ tsp. lemon or vanilla essence
- food colouring
- icing glue (see opposite page)

electric food mixer

greased baking tray

fish-slice

cooling rack

small bowl

rolling-pin

knife

Combine margarine, flour, sugar and lemon essence in a mixer to make a smooth dough.

Remove the dough and cut it into four equal parts.

Put one part back in the mixer with drinking chocolate and blend.

Divide each of the other three parts into three to make nine equal balls.

From the remaining ball roll eight small balls for noses. Flatten them and add to the centre of each face.

Flatten balls of chocolate dough onto the faces to make ears.

Add sultanas for eyes and one for nose.

For the bears' faces flatten eight of the balls onto the baking tray with the palm of your hand.

Bake for 12 to 15 minutes in a preheated oven. Allow to cool in the tin for one minute before removing with fish-slice to cool on rack.

Add a bow-tie when cool.

Hints

- Space the biscuits well, as the mixture spreads on cooking.

- If the dough is too crumbly after adding chocolate, add a few drops of milk to bind.

- If you have no food mixer, cream the fat and sugar together, then add the flour. Then continue as above.

Bow-ties

Put a few drops of food colouring in a bowl. Knead in ready-roll icing.

Roll it out. Cut oblongs and pinch in the centre, as shown. Stick on with icing "glue".

107

Cheesy scones

You will need: pinch of salt

225g (8oz)
self-raising flour

40g (1½oz) margarine

150ml (¼pt) milk

100g (3½oz)
grated cheese

slices of tomato

sieve

large bowl

rolling-pin

knife

scone-cutter 5cm (2in)

greased baking tray

Roll the dough on a floured surface.

Flour and margarine mixture should look like fine breadcrumbs.

Sift flour and salt into large bowl. Cut the margarine up and rub it lightly into the flour.

Stir in half the grated cheese. Add the milk and stir quickly with a knife to mix it in.

Push the dough gently together into a ball. Roll it out until it is about 2cm (¾in) thick.

Cut out circles with a scone-cutter. Put them on a greased baking sheet.

Sprinkle the rest of the cheese on top and bake for 10 minutes in the preheated oven.

Cut them in half. Fill with sliced tomatoes.

Cheesy twists

Oven: 190°C   375°F   Gas mark 5

Roll out some shortcrust pastry thinly. Spread half of it with yeast extract

and sprinkle cheese on top.
Fold the other half over the top of the filling.

Cut into strips, twist once, and lay on a greased baking tray.

Bake in a preheated oven for 10 to 15 minutes.

Hints

● Don't handle the dough too much, or it will become tough.

● If the oven is not hot enough the scones may not rise well.

Rice rabbit

You will need:

125g (4½oz) uncooked rice

fresh or frozen orange juice

50g ((2oz) sweetcorn

50g (2oz) cooked peas

½ chicken stock cube   water

50g (2oz) chopped ham

large bowl

rabbit mould 550ml (1pt)

saucepan

wooden spoon

clingfilm

large oval plate

You may need to drain the rice when it is cooked.

Cook the rice as directed on the packet, using half orange juice and half stock as the cooking liquid. Add ham and vegetables.

Line the mould with clingfilm, pressing it well into all the hollows.

Fill the mould with the rice mixture, pressing it firmly down with the back of a wooden spoon.

Put the plate over the mould and then turn both the right way up.

Serve with carrot sticks in a section of hollowed out cucumber.

Use shredded lettuce for grass.

Hints

• Make sure the rice is pressed firmly into ears, nose and tail before filling the rest of the mould.

• You could use cooked celery or broccoli instead of sweetcorn and peas.

Lift the mould off and carefully peel off the clingfilm. Eat warm or cold.

Christmas tree

You will need:

mild ginger biscuit dough (see page 128)

solid boiled sweets in assorted colours

flour

rolling-pin

non-stick baking parchment

greaseproof paper

felt-tip pen

flat baking tray

scissors

knife

plastic bottle-top or child's small pastry cutters

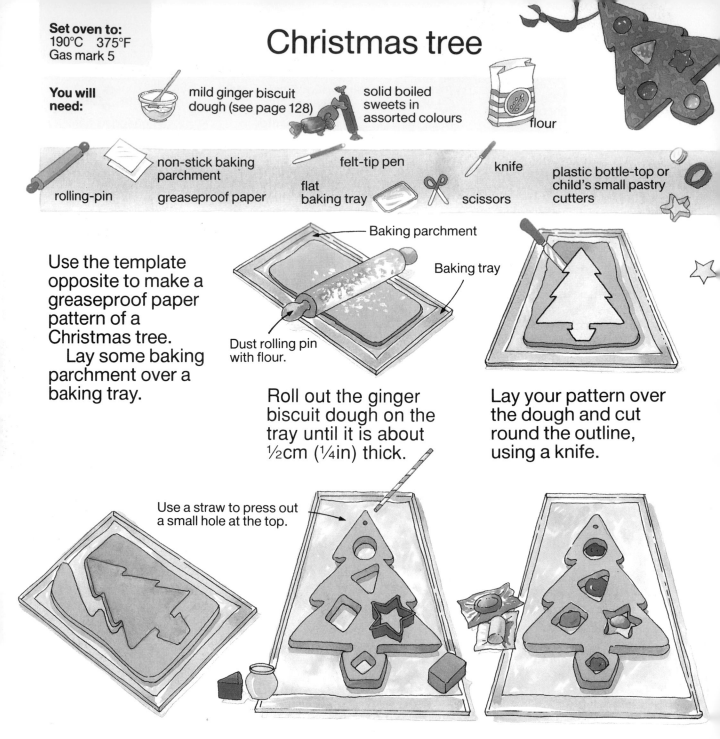

Baking parchment

Baking tray

Dust rolling pin with flour.

Use the straw to press out a small hole at the top.

Use the template opposite to make a greaseproof paper pattern of a Christmas tree.

Lay some baking parchment over a baking tray.

Roll out the ginger biscuit dough on the tray until it is about ½cm (¼in) thick.

Lay your pattern over the dough and cut round the outline, using a knife.

Lift the pattern off and carefully peel away the dough from the edges.

Cut shapes out of the dough tree, using a bottle-top or child's pastry cutters.

Bake in a preheated oven for 10 minutes. Take it out of the oven, place a boiled sweet in each cut-out shape and bake for a further five minutes.

For a marbled effect, crush the sweets individually by putting them in a plastic bag and hitting them with a rolling pin. Use several different colours in one shape so that they fuse together.

wool or fine ribbon

straw

Lay greaseproof paper over the template and trace round the outline with a felt-tip pen. Cut round the outline.

Template

Use biscuit cutters or saucers to make smaller stained glass shapes to hang.

Allow to cool on the baking tray, then carefully peel off the parchment.

Thread with wool or ribbon, then hang in a window or bright place so that the tree lights up.

Hints

● Be careful not to make the hole for the ribbon too near the edge of the dough. If you do it may break when you hang it up.

● The sweets will be molten and very hot on removal from the oven.

Try hanging several shapes from one ribbon. They will twist and turn and catch the light.

Cress creatures

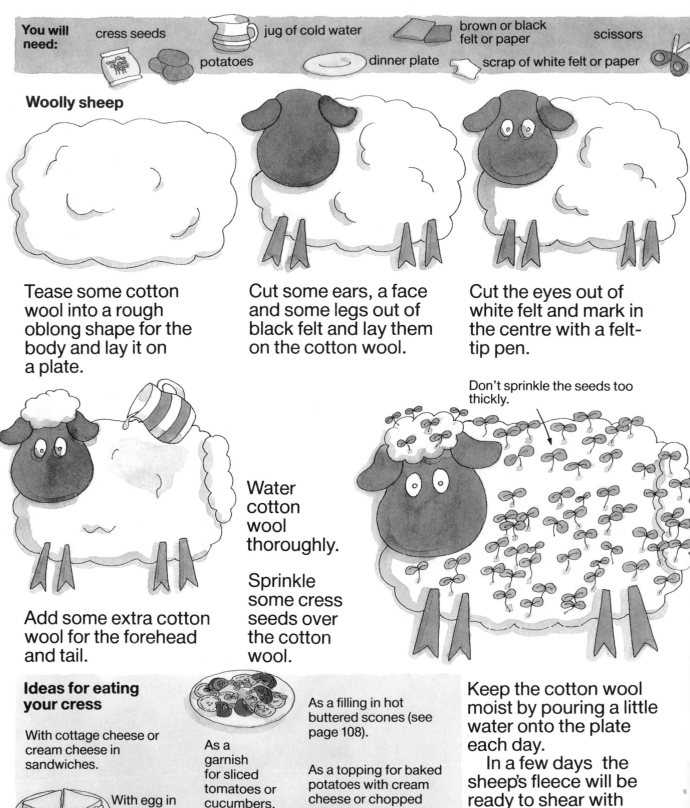

You will need: cress seeds — jug of cold water — brown or black felt or paper — scissors — potatoes — dinner plate — scrap of white felt or paper

Woolly sheep

Tease some cotton wool into a rough oblong shape for the body and lay it on a plate.

Cut some ears, a face and some legs out of black felt and lay them on the cotton wool.

Cut the eyes out of white felt and mark in the centre with a felt-tip pen.

Add some extra cotton wool for the forehead and tail.

Water cotton wool thoroughly.

Sprinkle some cress seeds over the cotton wool.

Don't sprinkle the seeds too thickly.

Keep the cotton wool moist by pouring a little water onto the plate each day.

In a few days the sheep's fleece will be ready to shear with scissors and eat.

Ideas for eating your cress

With cottage cheese or cream cheese in sandwiches.

With egg in sandwiches.

As a garnish for sliced tomatoes or cucumbers.

As a filling in hot buttered scones (see page 108).

As a topping for baked potatoes with cream cheese or chopped grilled bacon.

cotton wool · black felt-tip pen · carrot · potato peeler

Hairy caterpillar

Cut some bits of carrot to fit in the eyes, nose and mouth.

Scrub some potatoes. Choose a small one for the head and cut out a face with a potato peeler.

Slice the tops off the other potatoes. Scoop some of the potato out and replace it with cotton wool.

Water the cotton wool and sprinkle it with seeds.

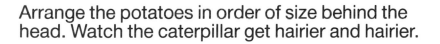

Arrange the potatoes in order of size behind the head. Watch the caterpillar get hairier and hairier.

Clown

Cut a slice from the base of a potato so it will stand. Cut out a face and insert a carrot-stick nose. Grow some hair on top.

Add pieces of potato for feet.

Other ideas to try:

Lion
Use orange felt and a frayed wool tail. Give him a cotton wool mane.

Stencils
Place a shaped biscuit cutter on cotton wool. Sprinkle seeds evenly inside them carefully remove cutter.

Names

Tease some cotton wool into fat strings and arrange in letter shapes on a plate.

Hedgehog
Find a potato with a pointed end for a nose. Cut out some eyes. Grow prickles on his back.

Hallowe'en lantern

You will need: large, ripe melon · orange crêpe paper · old newspaper · dessertspoon · two bowls · kitchen roll · sharp knife* · string · potato peeler · small torch

Newspaper will stop your working surface from getting sticky.

Spread out some newspaper and put the melon on it. Slice off the most pointed end with a sharp knife.

Scoop the seeds out into a bowl. Scoop the flesh from the melon and the lid into another bowl, leaving a shell about 1cm (½in) thick.

Cut out some eyes, a nose and a mouth, using a sharp knife.* Make some holes to thread a string handle through, using a potato peeler.

Turn the melon upside down and allow to drain for a few minutes. Use kitchen towel to pat the inside as dry as possible.

Line the inside with crêpe paper, covering the cut out shapes and pressing it against the sides. Thread string through the holes.

Switch on a small torch. Place it inside the melon, so the light shines through the crêpe paper. Put the lid on.

114   *For safety you could put a cork on the end when not in use.*

Easter nests

Set oven to:
190°C 375°F
Gas mark 5

You will need:

125g (4½ oz) flour

60g (2½ oz) margarine

60g (2½ oz) sugar

½ small beaten egg

mixed spice

food colouring

ready-roll icing or white marzipan

large mixing bowl

wooden spoon

sieve

garlic press

rolling pin

scone-cutter 6cm (2½ in)

flat baking tray

plate

Make a quantity of biscuit dough*. Roll out ½cm (¼in) thick on a flat baking tray.

Cut 6 rounds with a 6cm (2½in) scone-cutter. Remove the excess dough very carefully.

Squeeze the excess dough through a garlic press. Catch the strings of dough on a plate.

You could buy candy or chocolate eggs to fill your nests.

Lay twisted strings of dough round the edges of your rounds to make nests.

Bake for 15-17 minutes in a pre-heated oven until golden.

When cool, fill with eggs made from marzipan or icing with a little food colouring kneaded into it.

*See page 128 for recipe, substituting mixed spice for ginger.

Giant stripey bees

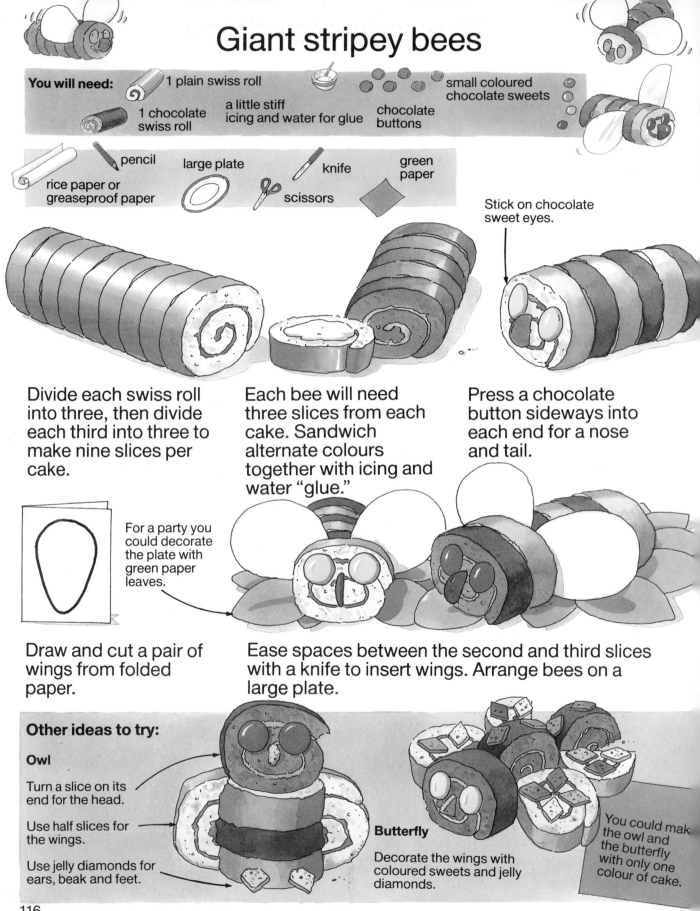

You will need:

1 plain swiss roll

1 chocolate swiss roll

a little stiff icing and water for glue

chocolate buttons

small coloured chocolate sweets

pencil

rice paper or greaseproof paper

large plate

scissors

knife

green paper

Stick on chocolate sweet eyes.

Divide each swiss roll into three, then divide each third into three to make nine slices per cake.

Each bee will need three slices from each cake. Sandwich alternate colours together with icing and water "glue."

Press a chocolate button sideways into each end for a nose and tail.

For a party you could decorate the plate with green paper leaves.

Draw and cut a pair of wings from folded paper.

Ease spaces between the second and third slices with a knife to insert wings. Arrange bees on a large plate.

Other ideas to try:

Owl

Turn a slice on its end for the head.

Use half slices for the wings.

Use jelly diamonds for ears, beak and feet.

Butterfly

Decorate the wings with coloured sweets and jelly diamonds.

You could make the owl and the butterfly with only one colour of cake.

Pink sunset pudding

You will need: grated rind and juice of 2 lemons

red food colouring

2 eggs, separated

1 tin condensed milk 400ml (15fl.oz)

100g (3½oz) castor sugar

2 large bowls

tin opener

electric whisk

wooden spoon

large metal spoon

ovenproof flan dish approx. 23cm (9in)

knife

Mix together the lemon juice and rind, egg yolks, condensed milk and a few drops of red food colouring.

In another bowl whisk the egg whites with a few drops of food colouring until stiff.

Whisk in half the sugar, then fold in the remaining sugar using a metal spoon.

Pour the milk mixture into a flan dish. Spoon the egg whites on top.

Flick into swirls and peaks using the knife.

Hints

•Make sure the bowl for the egg whites is dry and completely free of grease.

•This pudding tastes even better the day after you have made it.

•It can be used as a filling in a shortcrust pastry case, which has been baked blind for 10 minutes.

Bake for 12 to 15 minutes until crisp and lightly browned. Eat warm or cold.

Ham, cheese and pineapple slices

You will need: butter for spreading   4 slices thin-cut ham   4 small slices of bread

4 tinned pineapple rings   4 slices processed cheese

butterfly-type tin opener   kitchen roll   small bowl   butter knife   fish-slice

Press firmly on the bottom of the tin.

Open the tin and pour off any syrup into a bowl.

Use kitchen roll to pat the pineapple dry.

Using the tin as a cutter, press out four circles each from the bread, ham and cheese slices.

Toast the bread lightly on both sides under a grill, then butter it on one side.

Put a circle of ham, then pineapple on each round of bread, then top with cheese.

Using a fish-slice replace under the grill and heat until the cheese is melted and bubbling.

Hint

Use up any scraps of bread to make breadcrumbs in a blender. Use them for a savoury crumble topping or stuffing, or freeze them for later use.

Pretend pizzas

Toast some circles of bread, as above. Spread with a little tomato paste.

Sprinkle sliced vegetables and scraps of ham, salami or tuna on top.

Top with cheese and sprinkle sparingly with dried herbs. Place under the grill.

118

Hedgehog nibbles

You will need: a little milk · cream cheese · crisps · carrot sticks · savoury stick biscuits · cucumber slices · sultanas

large plate · wooden spoon · bowl · tea-towel

Rest the bowl on a tea-towel to prevent it slipping.

Beat the cream cheese with a little milk to soften it.

Put the cheese on a plate and pat it into a pear-shape with the wooden spoon.

Add sultana eyes and noses.

Press in vegetables, crisps, or savoury stick biscuits to make the hedgehog's prickles.

Hints

● You can make pink hedgehogs by adding a little tomato ketchup to the cheese.

● Try sweet hedgehogs, using pieces of tinned or fresh fruit for prickles.

Faces

Use a selection of sliced, shredded or chopped vegetables to create faces on bread circles (or rolls cut in half) spread with butter or cheese spread.

Sultana

Sweetcorn

Carrot

Cucumber

Radish

Cheese

Apple

Pepper

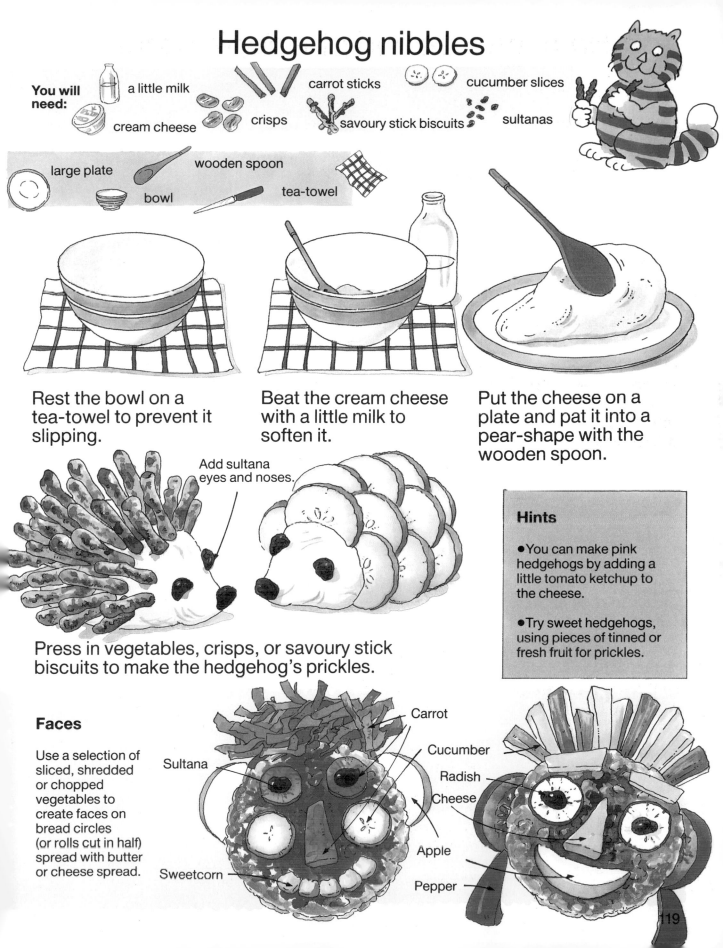

Dreamy drinks

Milk shakes

Whisk the ingredients together in a tall jug, using a hand whisk. Or use an electric blender, but don't remove the lid until the machine has completely stopped.

Use wide straws for thick shakes. If you want thinner shakes reduce the amount of ice cream and add ice cubes.

The amounts given will make enough for one adult and two children.

Hint

Save the juice from cans of fruit to make refreshing drinks. Dilute with water, fruit juices or lemonade.

Vanilla

Top with squirty cream and a glacé cherry.

Chocolate

Top with squirty cream and grated chocolate or chocolate vermicelli.

You will need:

300ml (½pt) milk

4 tablespoons vanilla ice cream

¼ teaspoon vanilla essence

300ml (½pt) milk

4 tablespoons chocolate ice cream

1 tablespoon chocolate dessert syrup

Other ideas to try:

Orange yoghurt drink

300ml (½pt) natural yogurt

juice of 2 oranges

2 to 3 tablespoons runny honey

Blend together as for milk shakes. Decorate with a slice of orange.

Ice cream soda

Fill a tall glass two thirds full of lemonade, or your favourite fizzy drink.
Add one or two scoops of ice cream and stir with a long spoon.

Strawberry

Top with tinned or sliced fresh strawberries.

Blackcurrant

Banana

300ml (½pt) milk

150ml (¼pt) strawberry yogurt

3 tablespoons strawberry ice cream

300ml (½pt) milk

6 tablespoons vanilla ice cream

3 tablespoons blackcurrant concentrate

1 ripe banana

300ml (½pt) milk

4 tablespoons vanilla ice cream

2 teaspoons honey

Squashy orange

Roll, squeeze and pinch a thin-skinned orange until it feels very soft all over.
Chill it, if you like, then poke a hole near the top with a potato peeler. Insert a short piece of straw and then drink.

Fun with ice cubes

Try freezing pieces of fruit, mint leaves, rose petals in ice to make decorative ice cubes, or freeze fruit juices to liven up drinks of squash.

Microwave castles

You will need: 140g (4½oz) self-raising flour · 75g (3oz) butter · 1 egg, beaten · 1½ tbsp. milk · ½ tsp. baking-powder · 60g (2½ oz) soft brown sugar · ¾ can blackcurrant pie filling · squirty cream

6 paper cups* · wooden spoon · large plate · large bowl · large metal spoon · knife

Stand the cups in a circle on a plate.

Cut up the butter and rub it into the flour and baking powder. Mix in the sugar.

Mix in the egg and milk and half the tin of fruit pie-filling.

Put half a tablespoonful of fruit pie-filling into the bottom of each paper cup.

Fill each cup with the flour mixture until about half full.

Put in a micro-wave** oven. Cook on "high", turning once, for about four minutes. Stand for one minute.

Hint

Use up leftover pie-filling as a hot sauce for ice cream. Heat it in the microwave.

Turn out the castles, then decorate with squirty cream.

122

*Don't use plastic cups. Some plastics give off dangerous fumes
**Do not use an ordinary oven.

Munchy mice

You will need: 250g (9oz) icing sugar • 125g (4½oz) dessicated coconut • pink food colouring • 200ml (7fl.oz) condensed milk • 6 pieces pink wool or red liquorice • flaked almonds • chocolate drops and jelly sweets

wooden spoon • clingfilm • large bowl • small bowl • pencil

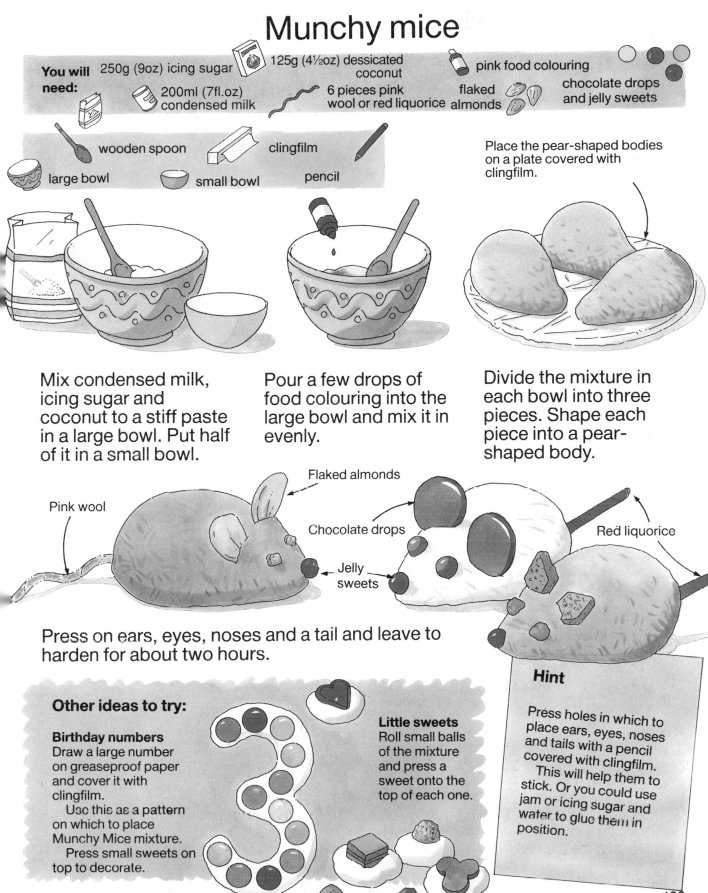

Mix condensed milk, icing sugar and coconut to a stiff paste in a large bowl. Put half of it in a small bowl.

Pour a few drops of food colouring into the large bowl and mix it in evenly.

Place the pear-shaped bodies on a plate covered with clingfilm.

Divide the mixture in each bowl into three pieces. Shape each piece into a pear-shaped body.

Pink wool

Flaked almonds

Chocolate drops

Jelly sweets

Red liquorice

Press on ears, eyes, noses and a tail and leave to harden for about two hours.

Other ideas to try:

Birthday numbers
Draw a large number on greaseproof paper and cover it with clingfilm.
Use this as a pattern on which to place Munchy Mice mixture.
Press small sweets on top to decorate.

Little sweets
Roll small balls of the mixture and press a sweet onto the top of each one.

Hint

Press holes in which to place ears, eyes, noses and tails with a pencil covered with clingfilm.
This will help them to stick. Or you could use jam or icing sugar and water to glue them in position.

123

Ice cream cake surprise

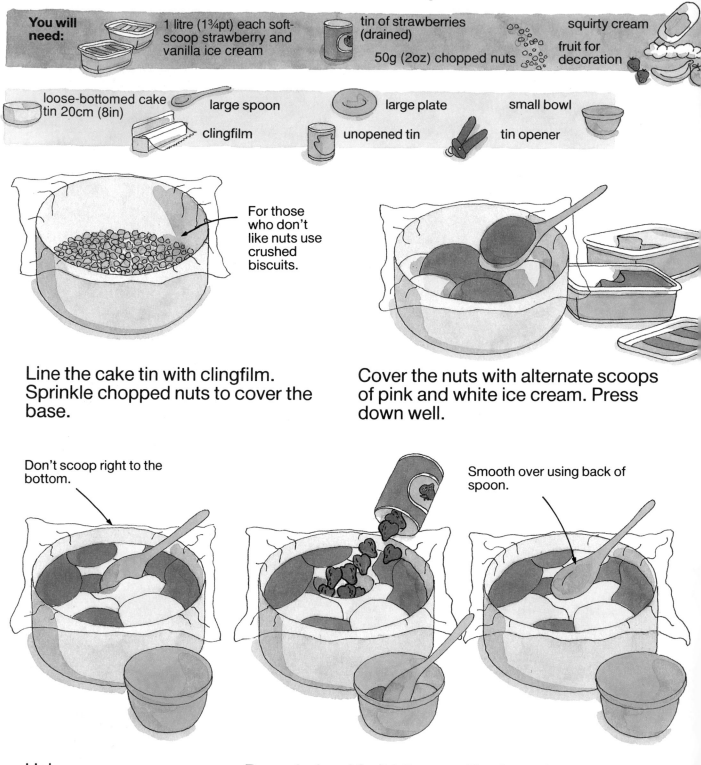

You will need: 1 litre (1¾pt) each soft-scoop strawberry and vanilla ice cream

tin of strawberries (drained)

50g (2oz) chopped nuts

squirty cream

fruit for decoration

loose-bottomed cake tin 20cm (8in)

large spoon

large plate

small bowl

clingfilm

unopened tin

tin opener

For those who don't like nuts use crushed biscuits.

Line the cake tin with clingfilm. Sprinkle chopped nuts to cover the base.

Cover the nuts with alternate scoops of pink and white ice cream. Press down well.

Don't scoop right to the bottom.

Smooth over using back of spoon.

Using a spoon, scoop some ice cream out of the centre into a small bowl.

Pour drained fruit into the hollow, almost to the top.

Replace the scooped out ice cream over the top. Freeze until firm.

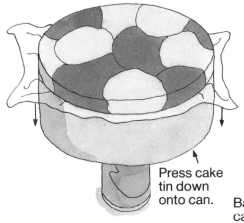

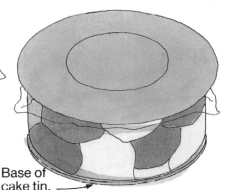

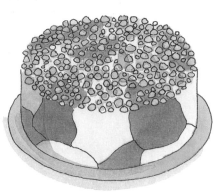

Press cake
tin down
onto can.

Base of
cake tin. —

To remove the cake
from its mould, press
the bottom of the cake
tin on to a tin can.

Put a plate on top, turn it over and remove the
cake tin base and clingfilm.

Decorate with squirty
cream and fruit.

Allow it to
soften for
about 30
minutes.
Cut as
required.

Other ideas to try:

Wafer surprise

Lay a slice of ice cream on a
wafer. Press into it a selection of
the following:

jelly sweets

slices of tinned or
fresh fruit

chocolate buttons

Press on a
second wafer
lid and freeze
until firm

Jelly-mould
ice creams

Hints

● Use oven gloves when
handling frozen tins to
avoid freezer burn.

● To cut ice cream use a
knife dipped in hot
water.

● To get ice cream out of
a mould, dip the mould
very briefly into hot
water.

● You can add crushed
meringues to the ice
cream if you like.

Use small jelly
moulds lined
with clingfilm as
ice cream
moulds. Press
down firmly into
all corners.

Banana lollies

You will need: firm bananas, runny honey, chopped nuts

new or sterilized lolly sticks, 2 large plates, clingfilm, saucer, knife, pastry brush

Pour some honey into a saucer and nuts onto a plate.

Insert a clean lolly stick into half a peeled banana. Brush it with honey.

Roll the banana in the nuts until it is covered. Sprinkle more over if necessary.

Arrange on a plate covered with clingfilm and then freeze.

Nuts

Crushed sweet biscuits

Try some other coatings.

Chocolate vermicelli

Dessicated coconut

Hundreds and thousands

Hints

● If the honey is too stiff, warm the jar (without its lid) in the microwave for a few seconds, or in hot water.

● You can use the handle end of plastic spoons if you haven't got any lolly sticks.

Take out of freezer 2 hours before eating.

Other ideas

Yoghurt melties

3 tablespoons frozen orange juice (unthawed)
6 tablespoons natural yoghurt
castor sugar to taste
3 tablespoons water

Mix all the ingredients together until mushy.

Pour into an ice-cube tray or the moulded plastic tray from a chocolate box.

Freeze. Turn out as needed.

Fruit lollies

Freeze fruit squash or the syrup from tinned fruit.

Don't forget to add sticks before freezing.

Drip-free lollies

When quite cool pour liquid jelly into small moulds such as egg cups or ice-cube trays.

Try layers of jelly and cooled custard or banana mashed with strawberry jam.

Parents' notes

Getting prepared

It is worth spending time on careful preparation before you start cooking to make things go smoothly. Get children into good kitchen habits from the start.

● Start by putting on aprons and washing hands.

● Clear a surface so that you have plenty of space to work on and show children how to wipe it down well.

● Gather all the ingredients and utensils before you begin and check them off together from the panels at the top of the pages.

● Prop up this book so that you can see your chosen page carefully. A cook's bookstand is ideal for doing this.

● To make clearing up easier put some old newspapers on the floor.

● If you will need the oven, set it to the right temperature before you begin.

Weighing and measuring

● It is a good idea to spoon dry ingredients onto scales rather than pouring them from a packet. There will be more control and less spillage.

● Instead of scales you could use a measuring jug, which shows levels for dry ingredients as well as liquids.

● Stand jugs and liquids on a tray. Drips and dribbles won't run all over your work area and need immediate clearing up.

● Children can measure spoonfuls of liquid from a bowl rather than pouring from a bottle. Tip measure into a small jug for easy handling.

Utensils

Jugs: Use plastic jugs for measuring or pouring wherever possible. They are safer and light to handle.

Bowls: should always be the right size for the job: egg-whites can quadruple in volume; flour and icing sugar can drift in clouds from a small bowl; china bowls hold steady for mixing and whisking. Small plastic bowls are easy to handle when adding other ingredients.

   To avoid slipping stand bowls on a tea towel while creaming and mixing. Small bowls are useful to take discarded egg shells.

   Put used cutlery blade end down into mugs.

Knives: Use round-ended knives wherever possible. If you need to use a sharp knife, put a piece of cork on the tip when not in use.

Tinopeners: Use the "butterfly" type if possible – they do not leave a ragged edge on the tin. Wrap lids carefully in double newspaper and discard immediately. To drain the contents of a tin pour slowly into a sieve over a bowl at least as wide.

Cutters: use plastic cutters. Metal ones are sharp and could be pressed into dough upside down by mistake, hurting a child's hand. You can also use plastic tumblers, washed aerosol caps etc. for cutting out shapes.

Wooden spoons: come in different lengths. Choose a short one for a child's use.

Food graters: plastic ones are safer than metal. Grating is quite hard work and children may tire of it quickly. Take over yourself when the item becomes too small to handle safely.

Electrical gadgets

These are great time and effort savers and there is no reason why a small child should not help use them with careful supervision. Never leave an appliance plugged in and unattended. Keep them well away from sinks and bowls of liquid.

Food processors: make sure the machine has completely stopped, before taking off the lid and removing the contents.

Egg whisks: use a high-sided bowl. For safety and to avoid the mixture flying off, switch beaters on and off while blades are inside the bowl.

Ovens

● Make sure that children are well aware of the dangers of a hot oven. Make an obvious show of wearing oven gloves even while just checking baking progress – the door and door knobs on some ovens can become quite hot.
● Ask small children to stand well back from an oven. There could be a blast of hot air in their face and they shouldn't get underfoot while you deal with hot food.
● Check that you have a clear heatproof space ready to take a hot dish before you you open up the oven.
● Use a fish slice for transferring food safely to a cooling rack.
● Some foods need to be cooled in the baking tray but make sure you place them well out of reach.

Freezers

Use oven gloves to avoid freezer burn, especially from metal containers such as cake-tins and ice-cube trays.

Microwave ovens

Be careful to stress that in some cases the container might be cool, but the contents very hot. Paper containers will feel very hot to the touch as the heat of the food comes through.

When using clingfilm in the microwave make sure it is the non-toxic kind especially for microwave use.

Foods

Flour: the recipes in this book use white flour. Other flours can be used, but may require more liquid to achieve the right consistency.

Food colourings: if you are worried about the effect of these additives, you can get non-artificial food colourings from health food stores.

Extend your range of colours by mixing various combinations before adding to the food.

To colour ready-roll icing put a few drops of colouring in a bowl and knead the required amount of icing into it until the colour is even. If the colouring makes the icing too wet, sift a little icing sugar into it and knead it in.

To colour ordinary icing make up the icing slightly stiffer than needed, then add the drops of colour a little at a time until the right colour and consistency is reached.

Mild ginger biscuit dough

125g (4½oz) plain flour
60g (2½oz) margarine
60g (2½oz) brown sugar
½ a small beaten egg
1 tsp ground ginger

● Beat the margarine and sugar together until creamy.
● Add the egg, a little at a time.
● Sift in the flour and ginger.
● Mix well to make a firm dough.
If it is too soft add a little more flour.

Victoria sandwich cake mix

100g (3½oz) margarine
100g (3½oz) castor sugar
100g (3½oz) self-raising flour
2 eggs

● Cream the margarine and sugar together until light and fluffy.
● Beat in the eggs gradually, adding a little flour each time to prevent curdling.
● Fold in the rest of the flour.

YOU AND YOUR CHILD
PAINT FUN

Children are fascinated by the feel and colour of paint and, with this book, adults and children can have fun exploring together a range of paint techniques and materials. All the projects are simple yet stimulating, ensuring hours of amusement while providing the context for many learning opportunities.

Munching monster

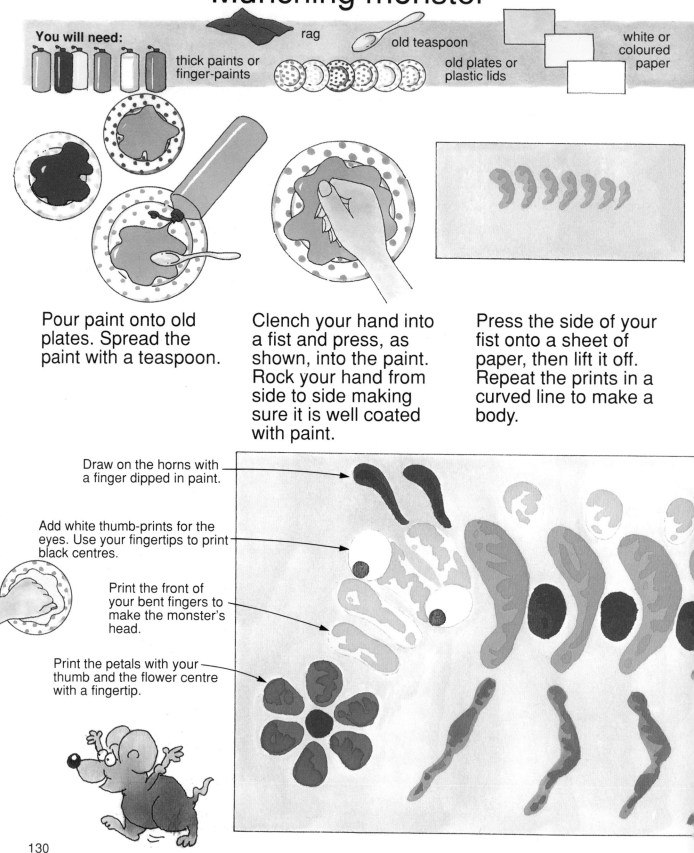

Pour paint onto old
plates. Spread the
paint with a teaspoon.

Clench your hand into
a fist and press, as
shown, into the paint.
Rock your hand from
side to side making
sure it is well coated
with paint.

Press the side of your
fist onto a sheet of
paper, then lift it off.
Repeat the prints in a
curved line to make a
body.

Draw on the horns with
a finger dipped in paint.

Add white thumb-prints for the
eyes. Use your fingertips to print
black centres.

Print the front of
your bent fingers to
make the monster's
head.

Print the petals with your
thumb and the flower centre
with a fingertip.

Other ideas

Bees on flowers

On yellow paper, use the front of your bent fingers to print black bees' bodies. Allow the bodies to dry and add white thumb-print wings. With a fine paintbrush, draw in the antennae. Print some big bright flowers.

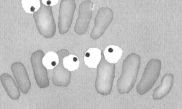

Big-eyed bugs

Print the bugs with the front of your clenched fingers. Finger print the eyes. Make your own greetings cards.

Spot-and-wipe dragonflies

Dip a finger into thick paint and then press onto paper. Pull the paint into a tail and then lift off quickly. Add some wings with the side of your little finger and draw in the antennae.

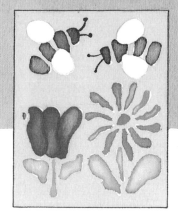

Wipe your hands with a rag in between colours.

Hints

• Before you start, print various parts of your hand to find all the different shapes you can make.

• Change hands to make 'side of the fist' prints curve in the opposite direction.

Print some decorations with your fingers and thumbs.

Finger print the tail.

For the legs, print the side of your little finger.

Rainbow fish

You will need:

large sheets of white paper — small household paintbrush — pot of water — ready-mix paints (including blue, green and white) — pencil — 2 saucers — egg box — round-ended scissors

Sea

Using a household paintbrush, quickly paint a sheet of paper with water.

Pour green paint onto a saucer. Paint a wavy green line across the top of the wet paper. Rinse your brush.

Pour blue paint onto another saucer. Paint a wavy blue line under the green. Repeat this until you reach the bottom of the sheet. Leave it to dry.

Fish

Draw a fat fish shape onto a piece of thin cardboard. Leave a wide edge.

Use the tip of a ball-point pen.

Throw away the cut-out piece.

Poke a hole in the fish. Insert the scissors into the hole. Cut to the outside edge, and then around the fish shape.

Lightly tape the stencil onto a white piece of paper.

Other fish ideas

Dab on stripes.

Print the corner of the sponge.

Print the edge of the sponge.

Fold the sponge so the edge forms a V shape, and use it to print.

132

thin cardboard

sponge
cleaning cloth

ball-point pen

sticky tape*

rag

paper glue

Cut at least 6 squares, about 3cm by 3cm (1in by 1in), from a sponge cloth.

Squeeze some paint into the holes of an empty egg box.

Dip a piece of sponge into the paint and dab lightly over the stencil.

Wipe the stencil both sides with a rag before making more fish shapes.

Other ideas

Birds in a tree

Paint a watery blue sky and a tree. Make bird shapes in the same way as the fish. Sit your birds on the tree.

Tulips

Make tulip shapes and glue them onto a grassy background. Draw in the stems and leaves.

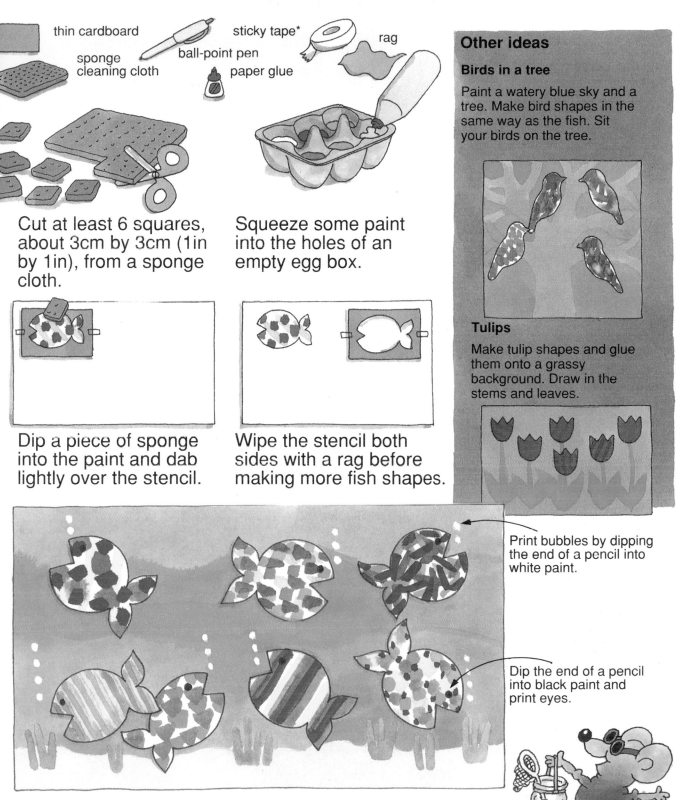

Print bubbles by dipping the end of a pencil into white paint.

Dip the end of a pencil into black paint and print eyes.

When the fish are dry, cut them out and glue them

to the background. Sponge print sand and seaweed.

*clear tape or cellophane tape (U.S.)

Surprise patterns

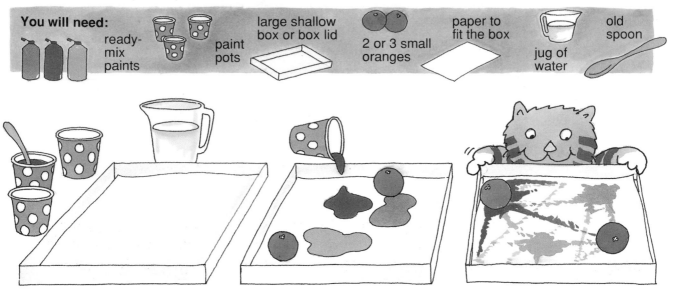

In the paint pots, mix each paint with a little water. Lay a sheet of paper inside a large shallow box.

Pour blobs of paint onto the paper and place two or three oranges into the box.

Tilt the box so that the oranges roll around, mixing and spreading the paint into patterns.

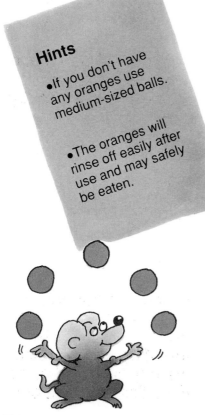

Hints

• If you don't have any oranges use medium-sized balls.

• The oranges will rinse off easily after use and may safely be eaten.

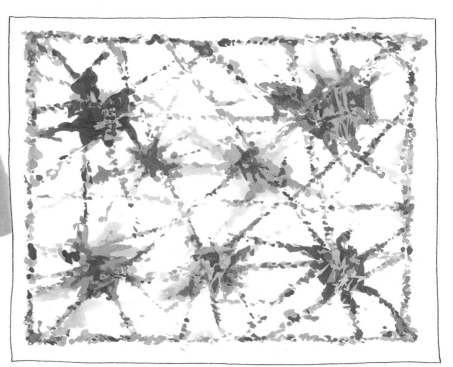

Remove the oranges. Now watch the colours change and merge as they dry. You could try this with undiluted paint.

Beautiful butterfly

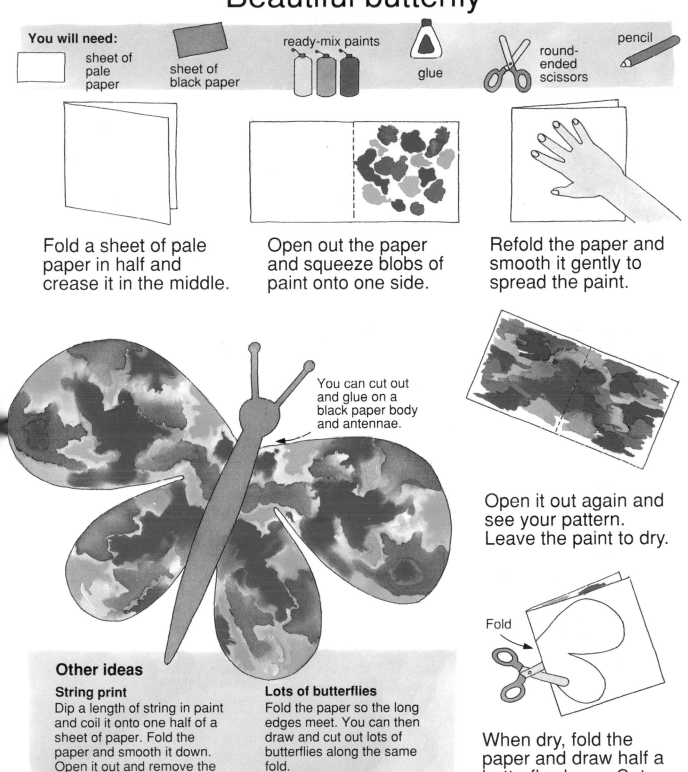

Fold a sheet of pale paper in half and crease it in the middle.

Open out the paper and squeeze blobs of paint onto one side.

Refold the paper and smooth it gently to spread the paint.

You can cut out and glue on a black paper body and antennae.

Open it out again and see your pattern. Leave the paint to dry.

Fold

When dry, fold the paper and draw half a butterfly shape. Cut the shape out leaving the paper joined at the fold. Then open it out.

Other ideas

String print
Dip a length of string in paint and coil it onto one half of a sheet of paper. Fold the paper and smooth it down. Open it out and remove the string to reveal a pattern.

Lots of butterflies
Fold the paper so the long edges meet. You can then draw and cut out lots of butterflies along the same fold.

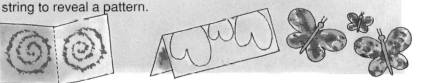

135

Fire! Fire!

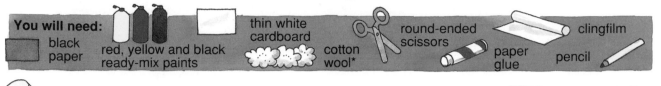

Squeeze red and yellow paint in wiggly lines on the centre of a piece of cardboard. Add a few squirts of black paint.

Lay a sheet of clingfilm completely over the cardboard. Dab the surface with cotton wool to spread and mix the colours.

Peel off the clingfilm from the bottom to the top. The paint will be pulled into flames.

Press wisps of cotton wool onto the wet paint for the smoke.

Using black paper, cut out and glue on a fire engine and other objects.

Cut doors and windows to show flames.

Hints

• Microwave clingfilm is firm and easy to handle. You could tape down the corners while you work.

• You can also make a print by pressing the peeled-off clingfilm onto a fresh piece of paper.

Arctic scene

Use cold colours such as blue, green, black and white to make an iceberg picture. Add cut-out polar bears, walruses and whales.

Stained glass shapes

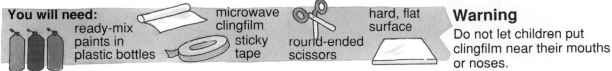

25cm (10in)

Cut a piece of clingfilm about 25cm (10in) long. Lay it on a flat surface and smooth out any wrinkles.

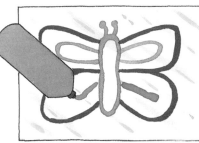

Squeeze paint thinly onto the clingfilm to make a shape. Leave a wide margin. Use lots of colours.

Carefully lay a second piece of clingfilm on top of the painted piece. Press down the edges.

Using your fingers, spread and smooth the paint.

Hints

• Shake the paint bottles well before you begin.

• This project does not work so well with ordinary clingfilm.

• Be careful not to use too much paint as it will sink to the bottom of your picture.

Press your clingfilm picture onto a window. Firmly dab the paint with your finger and see the light shine through the colours. Tape the bottom of the clingfilm to prevent any drips.

Wallpaper print

You will need: 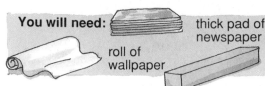 thick pad of newspaper

roll of wallpaper

long narrow box such as one used for clingfilm or kitchen foil

round-ended scissors

sponge cleaning cloth

sticky tape

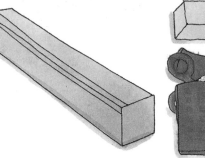

Close the lid of a long narrow box. Use sticky tape to seal the lid and cover any cutting edges.

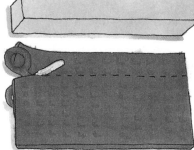

Cut a strip of sponge cloth the same width as the box.

Snip the strips into rectangles of various sizes. Cut the rectangles into different shapes, saving the leftover pieces.

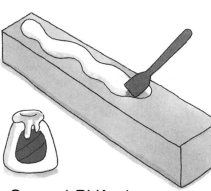

Spread PVA glue along the top of the box.

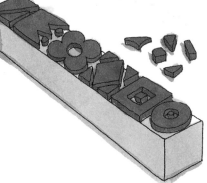

Press your sponge shapes into the glue. Use small leftover pieces in the gaps. Allow the glue to dry.

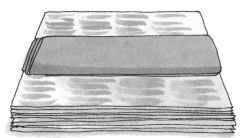

Fold a piece of cloth so it is a little longer and wider than the box. Place the cloth on a thick pad of newspaper.

Some printing ideas

Try printing with different kinds of cloth, such as corduroy, coarse wool and felt.

Print vegetables cut in half, or cut shapes into a halved potato.

See the shapes you can get by printing with pasta, pencil ends, crumpled paper, coiled playdough, corrugated cardboard and leaves.

138

PVA glue*
piece of cloth
glue spreader
old or plastic teaspoon
jug of water
ready-mix paint

Hints

• If you don't have any wallpaper use a large piece of paper or used computer paper.

• Cut centres out of the sponge shapes by folding them in half and snipping out the middles.

Moisten the cloth with a little water. Then squirt the paint, as shown, and spread it with the back of a spoon.

Press the box firmly into the paint and rock it from side to side to cover the sponges evenly.

Firmly press the box onto the wrong side of a piece of wallpaper. Then lift it off to leave a print.

Other ideas

Print a border on a paper tablecloth.

Print on tissue paper to make colourful wrapping paper.

Decorate a box with wallpaper prints to make a room for your toys.

Use two or more boxes to make colourful prints.

Continue to print down the length of the paper. You can try turning the box around to make a different print.

*See Parents' notes for U.S.

Giant sunflower

You will need: length of wallpaper about 1½ metres (5ft) long ∙ 3 old saucers ∙ green, yellow and brown ready-mix paints ∙ household paintbrush ∙ cotton wool ∙ newspaper

Weigh down corners if the paper curls.

Put one hand inside the boot while painting.

Lay a length of wallpaper on a long table or a washable floor.

Pour some yellow paint into a saucer. Now paint the sole of the larger wellington boot using a household paintbrush.

Press the boot firmly onto the top centre of the paper. Lift off to leave a print of the first petal.

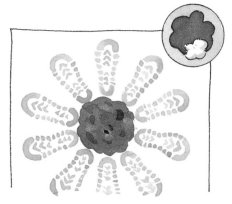

Rinse your brush.

Place a clean saucer directly beneath the petal. Using the saucer as a guide print a circle of petals, as shown. Repaint the sole of the boot before each print.

Remove the saucer and pour some brown paint onto it. Using a piece of cotton wool dab on a brown centre.

For the stem, pour some green paint onto a saucer. Roll up a newspaper and paint one side of it green.

Hints

● If your yellow is too pale to print well, mix in a little red paint.

● Rock the boot from side to side, and press the toe end down to achieve an even print.

● To clean the boots, wash them under a running cold tap and stand them on newspaper until dry.

pot of water

2 small wellington boots with patterned soles - in different sizes if possible

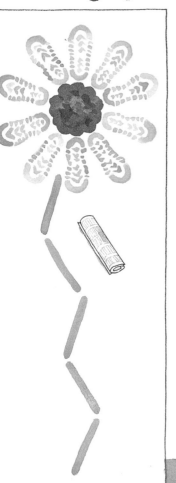

Use the painted newspaper to print a stem down the length of the paper. Try not to print a straight line.

Other ideas

Dragonfly
Print a body and large head using cotton wool dipped in paint. Print wings using large and small boots

Fish
Print a body and paint on a tail and fins.

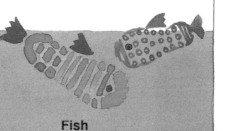

Bugs
Print the body and add on eyes and antennae.

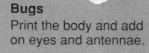

For the leaves, paint the sole of a smaller boot green. Use it to print leaves along the stem, as shown.

Rainbow string print

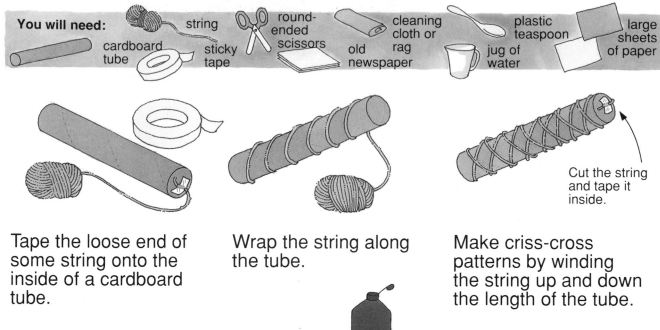

Cut the string and tape it inside.

Tape the loose end of some string onto the inside of a cardboard tube.

Wrap the string along the tube.

Make criss-cross patterns by winding the string up and down the length of the tube.

Fold a rag or cleaning cloth into a rectangle. Lay it on a thick pad of newspaper. Add a few drops of water to the cloth and let it soak in.

Pour four colours onto the cloth, as shown. Spread the paints with the back of a teaspoon. Wipe the spoon between colours with a rag.

Gently press and turn the tube in the paint, so that the string becomes coated.

Other ideas

Christmas decorations

Sprinkle glitter onto the wet paint and shake off the excess. When it is dry, cut out shapes to make decorations.

String patterns

Make your own printing blocks by arranging some string on a piece of glued cardboard. Press your string pattern into some paint and then use it to make prints.

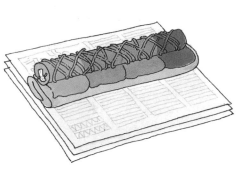

rag

4 ready-mix paints

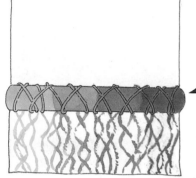

Put your fingers inside the tube.

Place the tube at the bottom of a sheet of paper. Roll the tube firmly away from you. Your string pattern will appear on the paper.

Wrapping paper

You can make your own wrapping paper by string printing onto tissue paper.

Repeat the rolling as many times as you like. Try printing with different coloured paper and paints.

Hint

The cardboard tube will stand a few washes under the cold tap. Pat it dry with a rag.

Autumn leaves

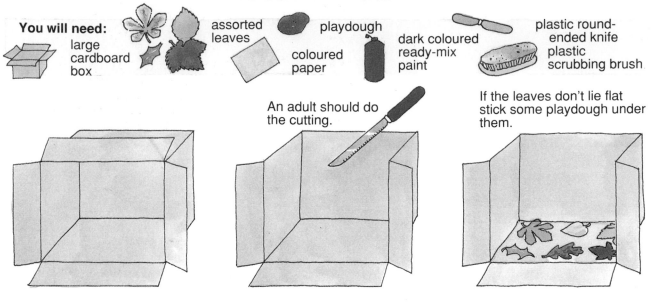

You will need: large cardboard box · assorted leaves · coloured paper · playdough · dark coloured ready-mix paint · plastic round-ended knife · plastic scrubbing brush

Lay a cardboard box onto one of its long sides. Open out its flaps.

An adult should do the cutting.

Use a breadknife to cut off the top of the box, as shown.

If the leaves don't lie flat stick some playdough under them.

Lay a sheet of coloured paper inside the box. Arrange some leaves on top of the paper.

Pour some paint into the dish and mix it with a little water. The paint should be quite runny.

Dip a scrubbing brush into the dish and gently shake off the excess paint.

Hints

● It is a good idea to let your child practise drawing the knife across the brush before any paint is applied.

● Take extra care when spatter painting to cover surfaces and wear overalls.

plastic spoon

breadknife

water

plastic or polystyrene dish (slightly longer than the scrubbing brush)

Other ideas

Make lots of single leaf shapes in different colours. Cut them out leaving a thick border of spatter paint. Make a leaf collage by gluing your shapes onto a sheet of paper.

Hold the brush in front of a leaf. Draw the blade of a plastic knife sharply towards you across the bristles.

Move the brush around as you spatter each leaf and the surrounding paper.

Try spatter painting with other flat shapes, such as keys, torn pieces of paper or small flat shells.

Keep the paper flat until the paint has dried. Then lift off the leaves. You will see the shapes of the leaves surrounded by spattered paint.

145

Marmalade cat

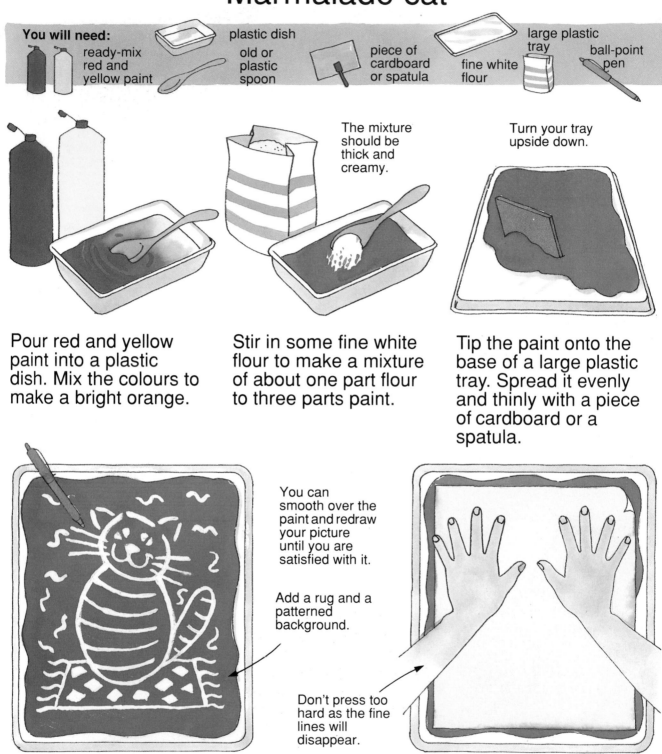

You will need: ready-mix red and yellow paint · plastic dish · old or plastic spoon · piece of cardboard or spatula · large plastic tray · fine white flour · ball-point pen

The mixture should be thick and creamy.

Turn your tray upside down.

Pour red and yellow paint into a plastic dish. Mix the colours to make a bright orange.

Stir in some fine white flour to make a mixture of about one part flour to three parts paint.

Tip the paint onto the base of a large plastic tray. Spread it evenly and thinly with a piece of cardboard or a spatula.

You can smooth over the paint and redraw your picture until you are satisfied with it.

Add a rug and a patterned background.

Don't press too hard as the fine lines will disappear.

Draw your cat into the paint using your fingers for the broad lines, and a ball-point pen for the thin lines.

Wash and dry your hands. Then lay a sheet of paper over the paint and, using the flat of your hands, smooth it very gently.

Hint

If you don't have a plastic tray use a smooth kitchen working surface. Afterwards, remove the paint with newspaper before washing.

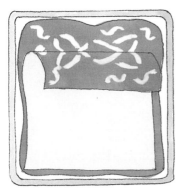

Lift up the top two corners of the paper and slowly peel it back. Be careful not to drag the paint.

Other ideas

Multi-coloured print

Try spreading two or three colours on the tray to make a multi-coloured print.

Window decoration

Make a print on a piece of tissue paper.

Lay a piece of ordinary paper on top of the tissue to prevent it tearing as you smooth it down. When dry, hang it by a window so the light shines through.

Leave the print to dry completely. You can varnish your print by painting it with PVA glue. The glue will be transparent when dry.

Wash the tray immediately after use. Remove any remaining stains with kitchen cleaner.

Magic colours

You will need:

1 large paper plate

pink, yellow, green and blue ready-mix paints

4 paint pots

small household paintbrush

pot of water

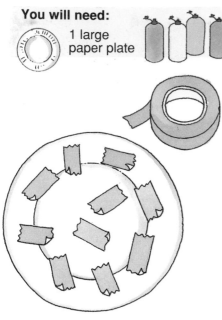

Tear off ten pieces of masking tape, each about 3cm (1in) long. Stick them on a paper plate leaving a corner sticking up.

In paint pots, mix each colour paint with some water. The paint should be fairly runny.

Brush pink paint over the plate and the pieces of tape. Allow the paint to dry.

Hints

● You can also use polystyrene plates.

● Speed the drying process by placing the plate in a microwave oven. Leave it on a high setting for one minute.

● When choosing your own colours always start with light shades and go on to darker colours.

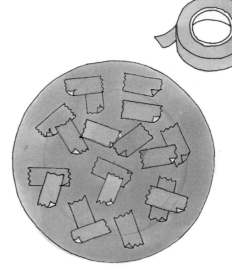

The fresh pieces of tape can overlap the painted pieces but don't cover them completely.

Stick another eight to ten pieces of tape onto the pink paint.

Cover the whole plate with yellow paint and set it aside to dry.

148

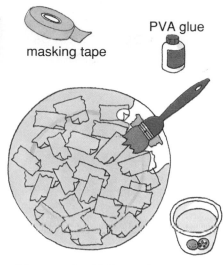

Repeat all the stages
using green paint and
leave it to dry thoroughly.

Tape the plate again in
the same way and paint
it blue. Then set it aside
until dry.

masking tape

PVA glue

Varnish the plate with
PVA glue. The glue is
white but is
transparent when dry.

Hang your plate
on the wall to make an
interesting decoration.

Peel the pieces of tape
away to reveal the
colours underneath. You

don't have to remove all
the pieces if you find a
pattern you like.

Other ideas

Use pale pink paint for
the first layer, then mix a
little red into the following
coats. The final layer of
paint should be pure red.
Experiment with different
shades of blue, green or
orange.

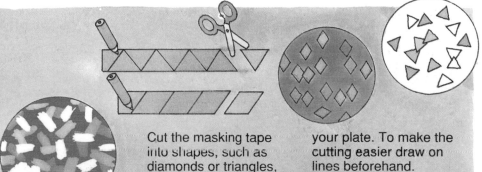

Cut the masking tape
into shapes, such as
diamonds or triangles,
to make patterns on

your plate. To make the
cutting easier draw on
lines beforehand.

Glowing flowers

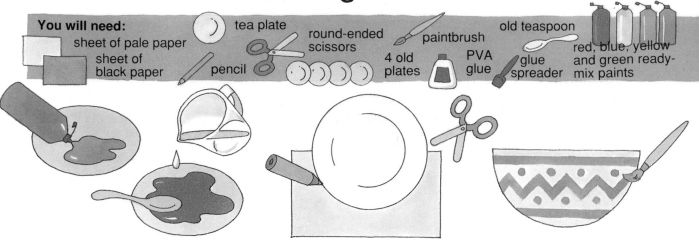

You will need:
sheet of pale paper
sheet of black paper
pencil
tea plate
round-ended scissors
paintbrush
4 old plates
PVA glue
old teaspoon
glue spreader
red, blue, yellow and green ready-mix paints

Pour paint onto four plates. Use one plate for each colour. Mix a little water into the paint and then spread with a teaspoon.

Place a tea plate half onto a piece of pale paper. Draw around the rim of the plate and cut out a bowl shape.

Paint a pattern on the bowl and leave it to dry.

You can dip the twists into two colours for an interesting effect.

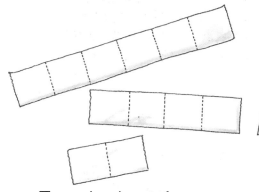

Tear six-sheet, four-sheet and two-sheet lengths of white toilet tissue. You will need about 18 lengths.

To make the flowers, fold the six- and four-sheet lengths of paper in half and then in half again. Twist lightly into rolls, as shown.

Roll the paper twists lightly in the paint. Then dip them quickly into a bowl of warm water and allow them to drip for a few seconds.

Other ideas
Family of snails

Blossom tree

Lady's hat

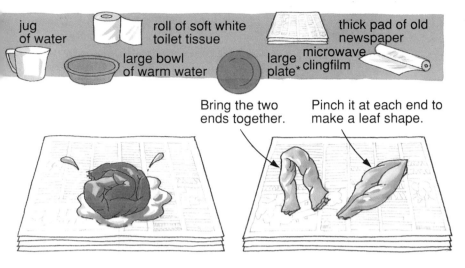

jug
of water

roll of soft white
toilet tissue

thick pad of old
newspaper

large bowl
of warm water

large
plate*

microwave
clingfilm

Bring the two
ends together.

Pinch it at each end to
make a leaf shape.

Coil the twists onto a thick pad of newspaper. Press the paper lightly so that a little water seeps out and the colour runs.

For the leaves, fold the two-sheet lengths of paper only once before twisting. Dip the twists into green paint and then the water. Shape them, as above.

Lay the flowers and leaves on a large plate covered with clingfilm. Place the plate in a microwave oven and cook on a high setting for ten minutes, or until they are dry.

Hints

• You can dry the leaves and flowers in a conventional oven. Place them on a baking tray lined with kitchen foil. They will take half an hour to an hour to dry in a moderate oven.

• For this project, you will need to cover surfaces with lots of newspaper and wear waterproof aprons.

Glue the bowl onto black paper. Arrange the flowers with the largest in the centre, filling in the gaps with leaves and smaller flowers. Glue them into place. Leave your picture to dry.

* Only use a plate recommended for microwave use.

Space bubble collage

Starry sky

Dot a piece of black paper with white paint to make a starry sky. Set aside to dry.

Bubble prints

Make sure the mixture is not too thick.

In a mug, make up some powder paint following the makers' instructions. The mug should be a third full.

Add a good squirt of dishwashing liquid and stir well with a teaspoon.

Warning
Before you begin, make sure your child can blow through the straw rather than suck.

Stir the straw round to make more bubbles.

Place a straw in the mug and blow until the bubbles rise above the rim.

Lay a piece of paper over the bubbles and press lightly. Lift off the paper without 'dragging' it. Allow it to dry.

Caterpillar

Overlap cut-out bubble prints to make a long caterpillar. Glue the shape onto some paper and paint on its eyes and feet.

Try some different coloured paper and paints. You could also print one colour on top of another for an unusual effect.

Materials (top banner):
sheet of black paper | paper glue | paints (including white) | round-ended scissors | paintbrush | pencil | round lids and bottle tops

Planets

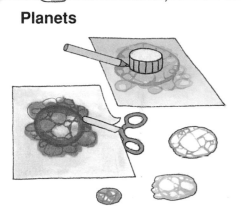

Cut out the bubble prints. These are your planets. Draw round lids or bottle tops to make smaller planets.

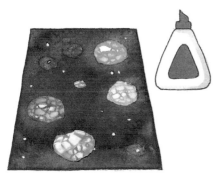

Glue the circles onto the starry background.

Hints

• You can use ready-mix paints for the bubble prints but they do not work as well.

• You could also make a starry sky by spatter painting (see page 144).

You could glue on a painted, cut-out alien and spaceship.

Dip your thumb into paint and print meteors.

Add spot-and-wipe comets (see page 131).

153

Dazzling snail trail

You will need:

red, green, yellow and blue ready-mix paints

4 paint pots

4 old or plastic teaspoons

tablespoon

fine white flour

saucepan

water

An adult should do the cooking.

Place one mug of white flour and three mugs of water into a saucepan. Whisk the mixture until it is smooth.

Place the saucepan on the heat and stir the mixture with a wooden spoon until it is thick. Leave it to cool.

Put a good tablespoon of the paste into each of four paint pots.

Add one colour paint to each pot and stir with a teaspoon. The mixture should feel thick and creamy.

Place the icing bag inside a tall plastic tumbler letting the top of the bag overlap the rim.

Drop in heaped teaspoons of the paint mixture, alternating the colours until the bag is half full.

Hints

- Practise piping on a piece of scrap paper before you start.

- Try different-sized nozzles to change the effect.

- You can use the flour and water paste as a glue.

- If the paint stains the icing bag, soak it in sterilising liquid.

This paint takes a long time to dry. Leave it in a warm room or hang it up with pegs - the paint won't run.

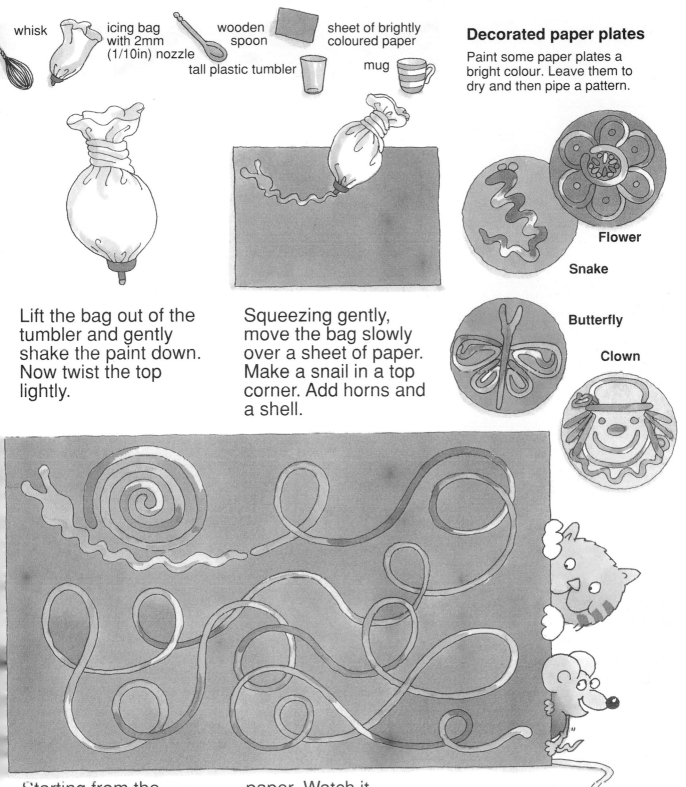

whisk

icing bag with 2mm (1/10in) nozzle

wooden spoon

sheet of brightly coloured paper

tall plastic tumbler

mug

Lift the bag out of the tumbler and gently shake the paint down. Now twist the top lightly.

Squeezing gently, move the bag slowly over a sheet of paper. Make a snail in a top corner. Add horns and a shell.

Decorated paper plates

Paint some paper plates a bright colour. Leave them to dry and then pipe a pattern.

Flower

Snake

Butterfly

Clown

Starting from the snail's tail squeeze a loopy trail all over the paper. Watch it change colour as you pipe.

Animal menagerie

You will need: 6 blown or hard-boiled eggs · darning needle · tea towel · bowl · water · sticky tape · cup · clingfilm · playdough

To blow an egg

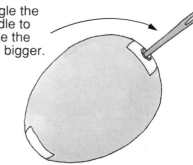

Wiggle the needle to make the hole bigger.

Wash the egg under running cold water and dry it gently on a tea towel.

Fix a piece of sticky tape on both ends of the egg.

Firmly push a darning needle, through the sticky tape, into the widest end of the egg.

Hold the egg over a bowl and pierce the opposite end. Wiggle the needle to break up the yolk. Peel off the tape.

Now blow hard through the top hole of the egg until its contents are forced out of the bottom*.

Hold the egg at a slant with the larger hole at the top and rinse under the tap. Pat it with a tea towel and leave it to dry before painting.

Boiling eggs

You can also paint boiled eggs. To boil an egg, place it in a pan of cold water and bring it to the boil.

Boil for 15 minutes and then place the pan under cold running water to cool the egg quickly.

* You can save and use the egg contents.

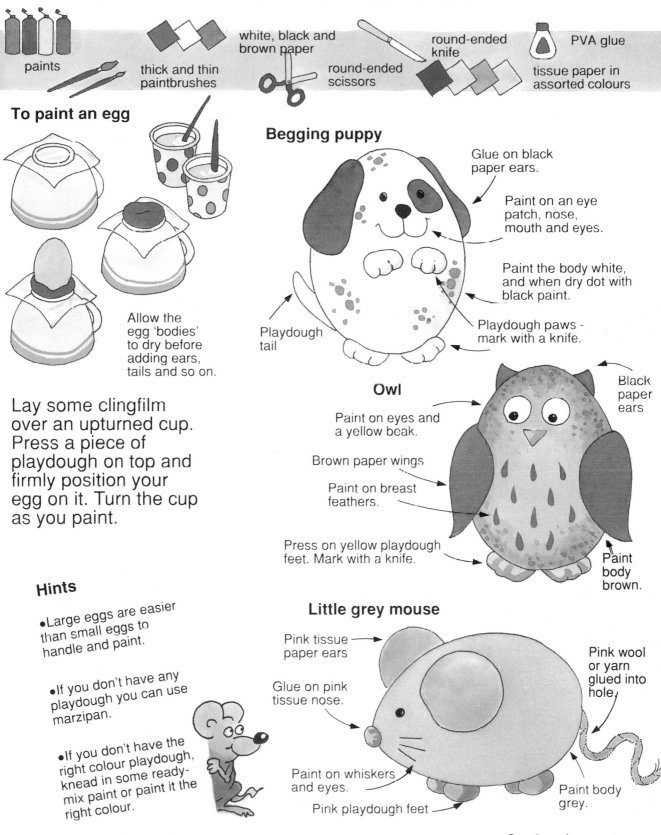

paints

thick and thin paintbrushes

white, black and brown paper

round-ended scissors

round-ended knife

PVA glue

tissue paper in assorted colours

To paint an egg

Allow the egg 'bodies' to dry before adding ears, tails and so on.

Lay some clingfilm over an upturned cup. Press a piece of playdough on top and firmly position your egg on it. Turn the cup as you paint.

Hints

• Large eggs are easier than small eggs to handle and paint.

• If you don't have any playdough you can use marzipan.

• If you don't have the right colour playdough, knead in some ready-mix paint or paint it the right colour.

Begging puppy

Glue on black paper ears.

Paint on an eye patch, nose, mouth and eyes.

Paint the body white, and when dry dot with black paint.

Playdough tail

Playdough paws - mark with a knife.

Owl

Paint on eyes and a yellow beak.

Brown paper wings

Paint on breast feathers.

Press on yellow playdough feet. Mark with a knife.

Black paper ears

Paint body brown.

Little grey mouse

Pink tissue paper ears

Glue on pink tissue nose.

Paint on whiskers and eyes.

Pink playdough feet

Pink wool or yarn glued into hole.

Paint body grey.

Continued on next page.

glue spreader

pink wool or yarn

cotton wool

paint pots

Pig

Pink paper ears

Playdough snout. Mark in holes for the nostrils with the end of a thin paintbrush.

Paint body pink.

Press on small playdough balls for feet.

Playdough tail

Animal mobile

Make a mobile by taping strong thread onto the eggs and hanging them from garden canes.

Easter rabbit

White paper ears. Paint the insides pink.

Paint on eyes, nose and whiskers

Cotton wool tail

Paint body white.

Place the rabbit on green paper.

Glue on tissue paper flowers.

Ears and wings

Cut the ears and wings from folded paper to make identical shapes.

To attach upright paper ears, bend the base of each ear back and glue the tab. Press onto the egg.

Cat

Finger paint paper ears.

Paint on fat white cheeks, nose, whiskers and eyes.

Finger paint the body orange and red.

Playdough tail

Playdough paws marked with a knife.

158

Witch's tree

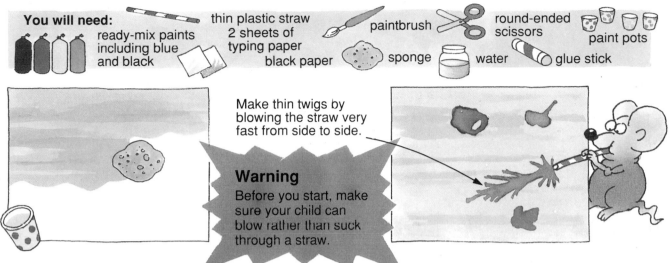

You will need:
ready-mix paints including blue and black
thin plastic straw
2 sheets of typing paper
black paper
paintbrush
round-ended scissors
sponge
water
paint pots
glue stick

Make thin twigs by blowing the straw very fast from side to side.

Warning
Before you start, make sure your child can blow rather than suck through a straw.

Mix some blue paint and water in a paint pot. Dip a damp sponge into the runny blue paint. Wipe the sponge across a sheet of white paper to make a streaky sky. Leave it to dry.

Pour some large blobs of runny black paint near the centre of the paper. Join the blobs and make a tree shape by blowing hard through a straw. Allow the paint to dry.

Hint
Make sure the blue sky is dry otherwise the black paint will sink in. Absorbent paper is unsuitable for this project.

Paint and cut out a witch, owl, cat, cauldron and a moon and then glue them onto your picture. Mount the witch's tree onto a black piece of paper.

Other ideas

Make a bright green jungle tree with creepers. Add thumb-print leaves and glue on painted cut-out animals and flowers.

Have a paint race with a friend. See who is first to chase their paint from one end of a piece of paper to the other.

Parents' notes

It is well worth spending a little time preparing your painting area. If possible, it is a good idea to work near a sink. Cover work surfaces and surrounding areas with old newspaper, and wear aprons or paint overalls. Have plenty of rags around for wiping brushes, hands and small spills.

Spills

Try to mop up any paint or water spills immediately to avoid any falls on slippery surfaces. If a large quantity of liquid is spilled, soak up the excess with an absorbent cloth then blot gently with another cloth. Remember some paint can stain; it is probably best to follow the manufacturers' instructions if paint is spilled.

Drying and displaying

Paintings will dry more quickly if you lay them on a cake rack, in an airing cupboard or by a sunny window. If you really want to speed up the drying process, place your painting in an oven set on a low temperature.

Displaying your child's work well will add to the pleasure of painting. Mount your picture by sticking it onto a larger piece of paper. Spend some time choosing a colour which will make the most of your child's work.

Colour mixing

The basic colours you will need are: black, white, yellow, blue, green and red. You can mix green but the resulting colour is not so bright.

Below is a colour mixing chart so you can experiment with different combinations.

Blue + red = brown

Blue + pink = purple/mauve

Blue + yellow= green

Yellow + red or pink = orange

Red + green = warm shades of brown

Green + yellow = acid green

Green + blue = dark leaf green

Basic materials

Paints

Paints should be non-toxic and water soluble. Ready-mix paints are suitable for many projects and can easily be thinned down. You can buy ready-mix paints from large newsagents*, art supply stores and shops selling educational aids and toys. Powder and poster paints are also widely available. Don't forget to read the manufacturer's cleaning advice before use.

Paint pots

These are sometimes necessary for mixing and thinning paint. Use old yogurt pots or similar containers to keep from buying them. Mix large amounts of paint in plastic ice cream tubs.

Brushes

A small household paintbrush is useful for painting large areas. You also need thick and thin children's brushes.

Glue

PVA (polyvinyl acetate)** can be used as a glue or brushed over paint to varnish it. It is white but dries transparent. PVA glue also adds strength to painted work and protects surfaces. Glue sticks are clean to use and the glue is easily directed.

Paper

Packs of coloured play paper can be bought quite cheaply. Cartridge and typing paper are less absorbent and are suitable for certain projects. Breakfast cereal boxes make a good source of thin cardboard.

160 *hobby shops (U.S.) ** all-purpose glue (U.S.)*

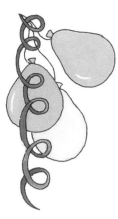

YOU AND YOUR CHILD
PARTIES

A party is a new and exciting extension of a child's expanding world. Parents and children can have fun preparing and enjoying the occasion together, and this book provides lots of ideas for giving and for attending parties. Much of the pleasure is in the anticipation of such events, and children can be happily involved in all the preparations while learning new skills and making their own contribution.

Pull-out fish invitations

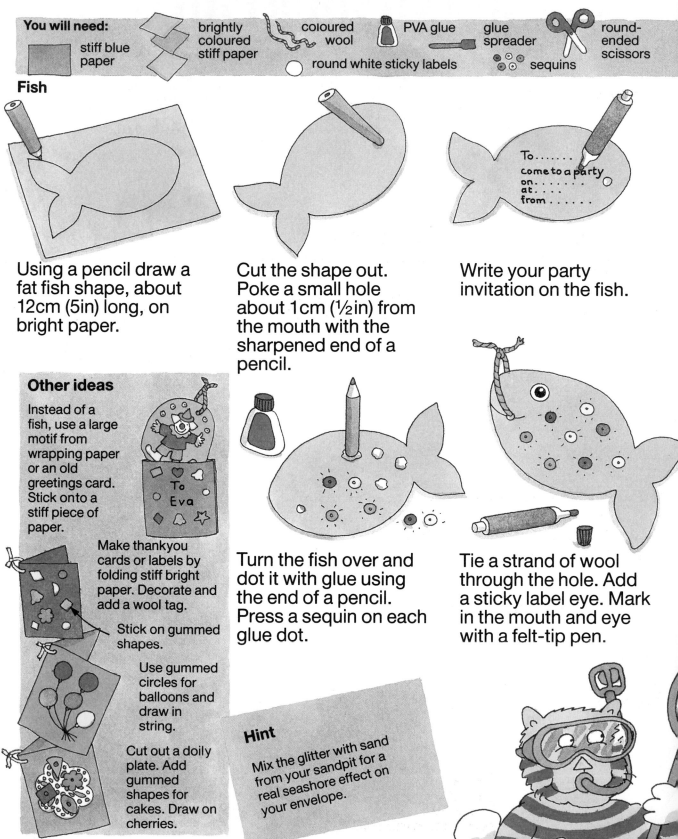

You will need: stiff blue paper, brightly coloured stiff paper, coloured wool, PVA glue, glue spreader, round-ended scissors, round white sticky labels, sequins

Fish

Using a pencil draw a fat fish shape, about 12cm (5in) long, on bright paper.

Cut the shape out. Poke a small hole about 1cm (½in) from the mouth with the sharpened end of a pencil.

Write your party invitation on the fish.

To.......
come to a party
on.......
at....
from......

Other ideas

Instead of a fish, use a large motif from wrapping paper or an old greetings card. Stick onto a stiff piece of paper.

To Eva

Make thankyou cards or labels by folding stiff bright paper. Decorate and add a wool tag.

Stick on gummed shapes.

Use gummed circles for balloons and draw in string.

Cut out a doily plate. Add gummed shapes for cakes. Draw on cherries.

Turn the fish over and dot it with glue using the end of a pencil. Press a sequin on each glue dot.

Tie a strand of wool through the hole. Add a sticky label eye. Mark in the mouth and eye with a felt-tip pen.

Hint

Mix the glitter with sand from your sandpit for a real seashore effect on your envelope.

162

black
felt-tip
pen
old newspaper
pencil
glitter

Envelope

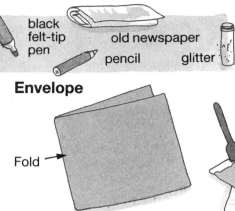

Cut a piece of blue
paper 35cm (14in) long
15cm (6in) wide. Fold
in half, as shown, and
crease the edge.

Open it out again and,
working on newspaper,
spread glue along the
long edges. Refold the
paper and press the
edges together.

Slide the fish into the
envelope leaving the
wool tag showing.

Draw a wavy line about
4cm (2in) from the
bottom edge. Spread
glue below the drawn
line.

Sprinkle the area with
glitter and shake off
the excess.

To
Jess

Write your guest's
name on the envelope
and stick on some
more sequins. Leave it
to dry.

Other ways to decorate your fish

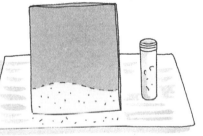

Stick on
gummed
paper
shapes.

Stick on torn tissue,
overlapping the colours.

Print stripes using the
edge of corrugated
cardboard which has
been pressed into paint.

Print scales using
plastic 'bubble'
packaging.

Pencil-top prizes

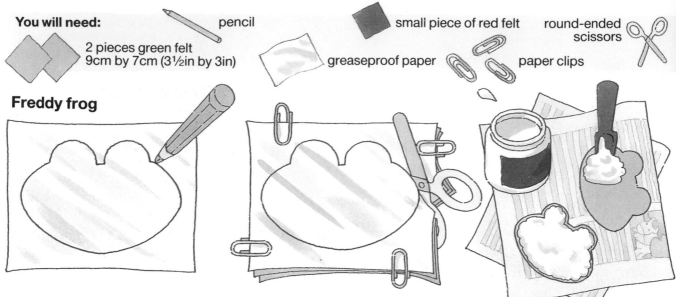

You will need:

pencil

2 pieces green felt
9cm by 7cm (3½in by 3in)

small piece of red felt

round-ended
scissors

greaseproof paper

paper clips

Freddy frog

Lay greaseproof paper over the frog template*. Trace round the outline using a pencil.

Fix the tracing onto two layers of green felt using paper clips. Carefully cut out the head and then remove the paper.

Working on old newspaper, spread some glue on each cut-out shape. Spread evenly to cover right to the edges.

Spread glue over 2½cm (1in) of the unsharpened end of a new pencil. Lay the glued end onto one shape, as shown.

Carefully press the second shape on top and ease the edges so they meet exactly. Allow the glue to dry.

Stick on two labels for eyes, as shown. Mark in the centres with a black felt-tip pen.

old newspaper

PVA glue

glue spreader

new pencil

round white stick-on labels

black felt-tip pen

Give your frog a sleepy look.

Add a wide mouth and nostrils. Glue on a bow-tie cut from a scrap of red felt.

Glue on some felt buttons.

Other ideas to try

Badge

Use sticking plaster to fix a safety pin onto a single layer felt face.

Hairband

Glue a single layer felt face, slightly off-centre, onto a smooth hairband.

Finger puppet

Leave an unglued area in the centre of the shape big enough to insert a finger.

Other animal pencil-tops

Cat

Use grey felt for a cat pencil top*. Add green felt for the eyes and a pink felt nose. Draw in face as shown.

Duck

Cut out a yellow felt face using the duck template*. Glue on an orange beak and use labels for eyes and mark as shown.

Rabbit

Make a rabbit face out of white felt*. Use pink felt for the nose and inner ears. Draw in the face with a black felt-tip pen.

Pig

Use pink felt for a pig*. Glue on ears and a snout. Use half labels for eyes. Mark in the eyes and nose with a felt-tip pen.

Balloon people

Blow up some balloons and knot the ends. Don't make them too full.

Cut some eyes, noses and ears from old magazines.

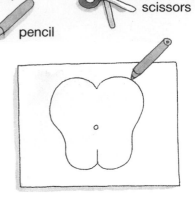

Lay some greaseproof paper over the balloon feet template* and, using a pencil, carefully trace the shape.

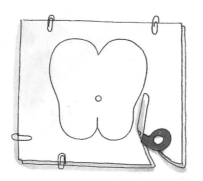

Cut a slit here.

Secure the tracing onto a piece of cardboard with paper clips and cut out the feet.

Poke a hole, as marked, using the sharpened end of a pencil.

Push the knotted end of a balloon through the hole.

Hints

● Keep balloons fairly small so they will balance easily on the feet, and be less likely to burst.

● It can be easier to apply glue directly onto the balloon, rather than pasting the paper and wool.

● Guests arriving at a party can decorate their own balloon. Prepare the feet in advance. To make lots of feet use the first pair as a pattern to draw round.

● To pop balloons without a bang, stick on a small piece of sticky tape and prick with a pin.

Stretch the knot backwards through the slit, as shown.

*See templates on pages 190-191.

PVA glue glue spreader

sticky tape

cotton wool

old magazines

wool strands

Tape the knot onto the back of the balloon.

Stand the balloon on its feet. Decorate it with glued-on eyes, nose and mouth . Glue on cotton wool and wool strands for hair .

You can colour in the feet.

Warning

Never allow children to put bits of burst balloon near their mouths or noses. This can cause suffocation.

Clown take-home picture

Provide lots of thick felt-tip pens and sheets of paper. Draw and colour large clown faces. Poke a hole in the centre with the sharpened end of a pencil. Push the knotted end of a slightly inflated red balloon through the hole to make a shiny nose. Secure the knot at the back with sticky tape.

Balloon nose

Balloon games

Throw two or three balloons into the air and see how long you can keep them up.

Give everyone a long and a round balloon. They must try and 'bat' a round balloon into a cardboard box turned on its side. First one in is the winner. Winners are easier to identify if you match the colours of the 'bat' and 'ball'.

Other ideas

Stick gummed paper shapes onto balloons to decorate.

Use balloons as party invitations. Attach an uninflated balloon to the front of a card with double-sided sticky tape. Write 'You and your balloon are invited to . . .'

Crocodile mosaic cake

Set oven to:
180°C 350°F
Gas mark 4

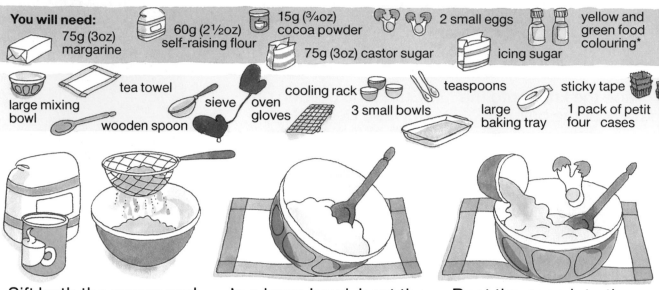

You will need:
75g (3oz) margarine
60g (2½oz) self-raising flour
15g (¾oz) cocoa powder
2 small eggs
yellow and green food colouring*
75g (3oz) castor sugar
icing sugar

large mixing bowl
tea towel
wooden spoon
sieve
oven gloves
cooling rack
3 small bowls
teaspoons
large baking tray
sticky tape
1 pack of petit four cases

Sift both the cocoa and the flour into a small bowl.

In a large bowl, beat the margarine and sugar until light and fluffy. Stand the bowl on a tea towel to prevent it slipping.

Beat the eggs into the mixture, one at a time, adding a little flour and cocoa with each.

Add the remaining flour and cocoa to the mixture. Stir well.

Place the petit four cases on a baking tray. Half fill them with the cake mixture.

Bake the cakes in a pre-heated oven for 15 to 20 minutes, or until the centres feel springy. Place them on a cooling rack.

Sift a little icing sugar, enough for two cakes, into a bowl. Mix it with a few drops of water.

Add a very small amount of yellow food colouring to the icing and mix it well.

In another bowl, mix a larger amount of green icing for the remaining cakes.

168   *You can buy natural food colours from health food stores.*

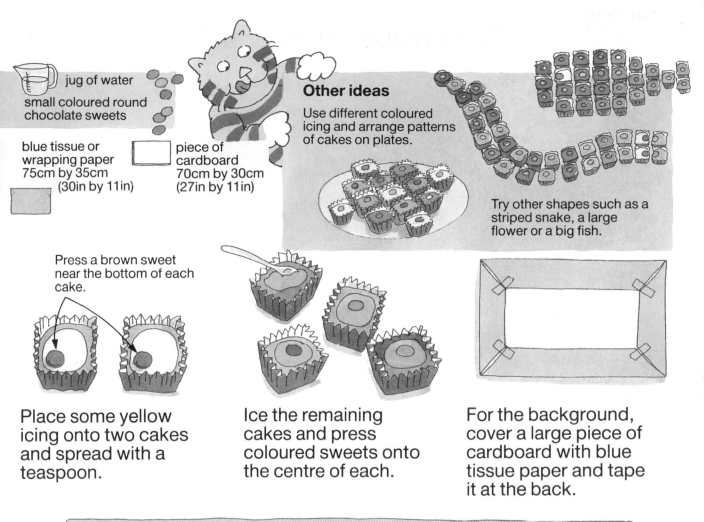

jug of water

small coloured round chocolate sweets

blue tissue or wrapping paper 75cm by 35cm (30in by 11in)

piece of cardboard 70cm by 30cm (27in by 11in)

Other ideas

Use different coloured icing and arrange patterns of cakes on plates.

Try other shapes such as a striped snake, a large flower or a big fish.

Press a brown sweet near the bottom of each cake.

Place some yellow icing onto two cakes and spread with a teaspoon.

Ice the remaining cakes and press coloured sweets onto the centre of each.

For the background, cover a large piece of cardboard with blue tissue paper and tape it at the back.

Arrange the cakes on the blue tissue paper in a crocodile shape, as shown.

Cut out tissue paper reeds and fish to decorate the 'river'.

Hints

• If you don't have a large piece of cardboard simply lay the blue paper on a table and arrange the shape.

• 30 cakes will be enough for about 10 children. Increase the number of cakes and lengthen the crocodile if necessary. Leftover cakes can go in party take-home bags.

Octopus tablecloth

You will need:

thick water-based paints in various colours

old newspaper

large paper plates (or old plates) 1 per colour

pieces of thick cotton or wool cloth

fat drinking straw

plastic fork

Printing pads

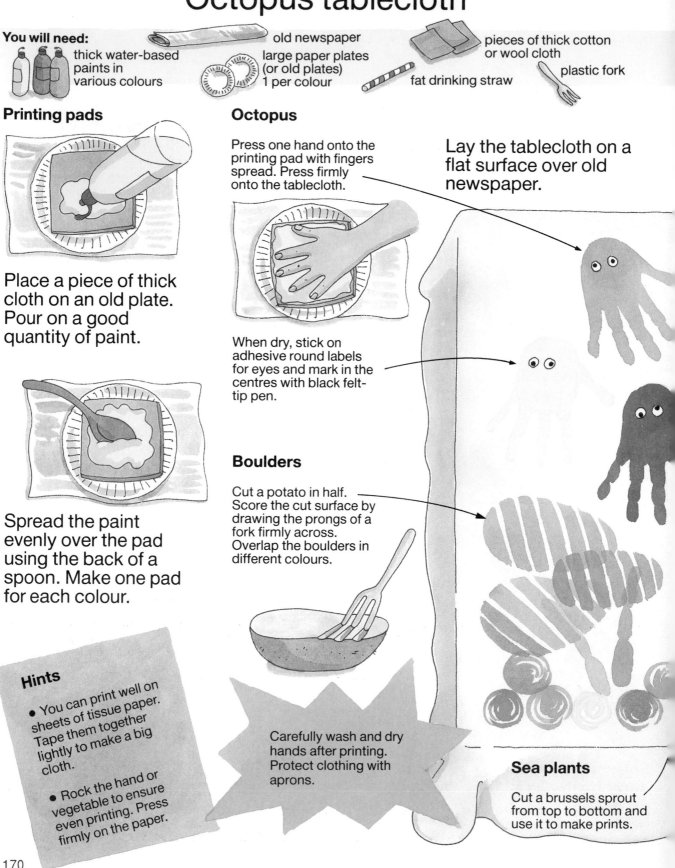

Place a piece of thick cloth on an old plate. Pour on a good quantity of paint.

Spread the paint evenly over the pad using the back of a spoon. Make one pad for each colour.

Octopus

Press one hand onto the printing pad with fingers spread. Press firmly onto the tablecloth.

When dry, stick on adhesive round labels for eyes and mark in the centres with black felt-tip pen.

Boulders

Cut a potato in half. Score the cut surface by drawing the prongs of a fork firmly across. Overlap the boulders in different colours.

Lay the tablecloth on a flat surface over old newspaper.

Hints

- You can print well on sheets of tissue paper. Tape them together lightly to make a big cloth.

- Rock the hand or vegetable to ensure even printing. Press firmly on the paper.

Carefully wash and dry hands after printing. Protect clothing with aprons.

Sea plants

Cut a brussels sprout from top to bottom and use it to make prints.

old spoon

black felt-tip pen

round, white stick-on labels

brussels sprout

fork

round-ended knife

potato

fat carrot

white or pale paper tablecloth

Little fish

Use the pad of your thumb to print the body. Make a tail using the end of your forefinger.

Mark in eyes and mouth with a felt-tip pen. For the bubbles, print the end of a fat straw.

Other ideas

Print octopuses onto paper cups. Mix the paint with a little PVA glue to make it waterproof.

Print giant flowers using halved apples for centres. Hand print the petals.

Print striped caterpillars (see striped shell). Use labels for eyes. Print the underside of large leaves for the background.

Striped shells

Cut the end off a fat carrot. Slice the carrot in half, as shown, and then cut slanting stripes.

Seaweed

Press the side of your hand into the paint and print with it.

Rocks and pebbles

Print slices of carrot for rocks and pebbles.

Push a fork into the back for a handle when printing. Wash and dry carrot between colours.

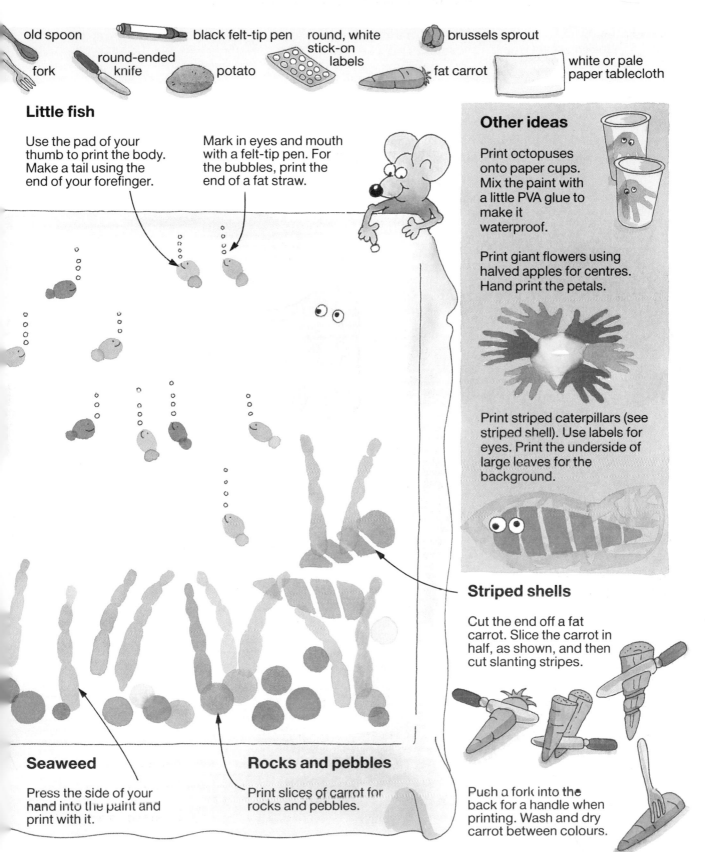

Jumping teddy

You will need: pencil, ruler, piece of stiff yellow paper 40cm by 46cm (16in by 18in), saucer, round-ended scissors, plastic or paper cup, PVA glue, glue spreader, 2 small and 1 large black button, drawing pin

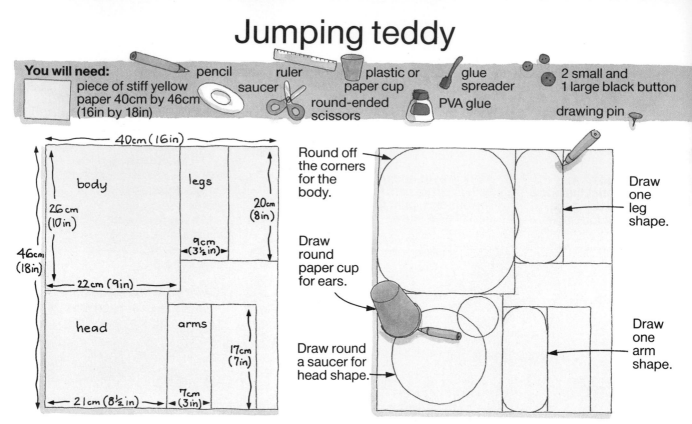

Round off the corners for the body.

Draw one leg shape.

Draw round paper cup for ears.

Draw round a saucer for head shape.

Draw one arm shape.

Using a pencil and ruler, measure and draw rectangles on stiff yellow paper.

Draw body shapes, as shown. Cut out all the rectangles and the head and body shapes.

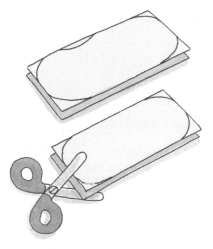

Place the drawn leg over the other leg piece. Cut out two legs. Do the same for the arms.

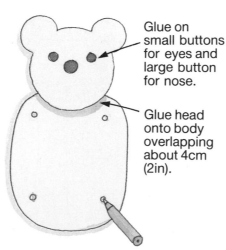

Glue on small buttons for eyes and large button for nose.

Glue head onto body overlapping about 4cm (2in).

Glue on the head and buttons and leave to dry. Poke holes in the body with a sharp pencil point.

Working on newspaper, paint the paws and inside of the ears brown. Paint a red T-shirt on the arms and the body.

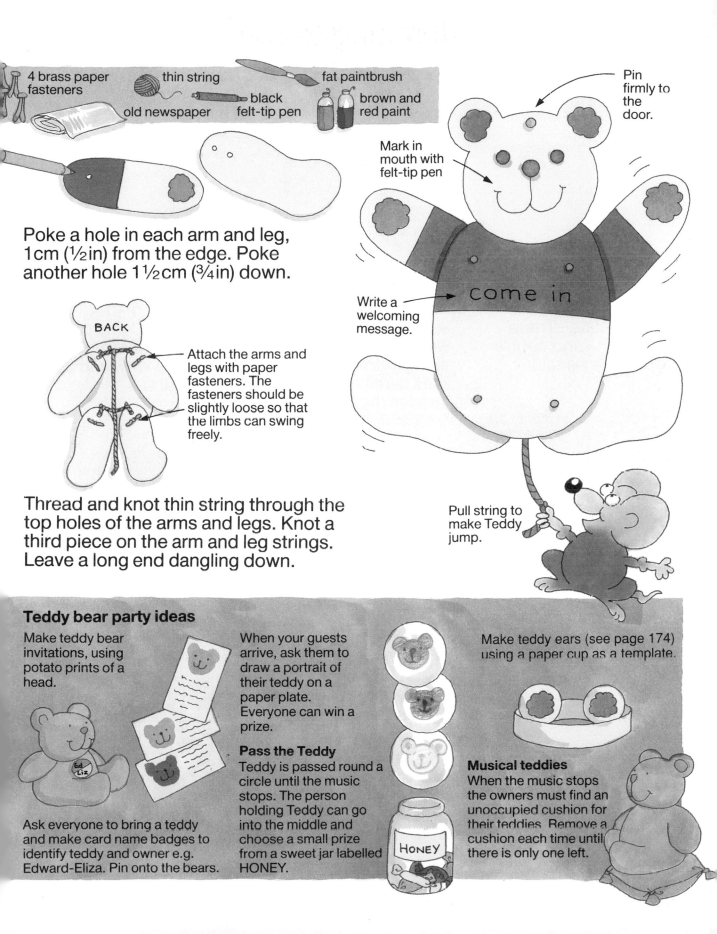

4 brass paper fasteners

thin string

old newspaper

black felt-tip pen

fat paintbrush

brown and red paint

Poke a hole in each arm and leg, 1cm (½in) from the edge. Poke another hole 1½cm (¾in) down.

BACK

Attach the arms and legs with paper fasteners. The fasteners should be slightly loose so that the limbs can swing freely.

Thread and knot thin string through the top holes of the arms and legs. Knot a third piece on the arm and leg strings. Leave a long end dangling down.

Pin firmly to the door.

Mark in mouth with felt-tip pen

Write a welcoming message.

come in

Pull string to make Teddy jump.

Teddy bear party ideas

Make teddy bear invitations, using potato prints of a head.

Ask everyone to bring a teddy and make card name badges to identify teddy and owner e.g. Edward-Eliza. Pin onto the bears.

When your guests arrive, ask them to draw a portrait of their teddy on a paper plate. Everyone can win a prize.

Pass the Teddy
Teddy is passed round a circle until the music stops. The person holding Teddy can go into the middle and choose a small prize from a sweet jar labelled HONEY.

HONEY

Make teddy ears (see page 174) using a paper cup as a template.

Musical teddies
When the music stops the owners must find an unoccupied cushion for their teddies. Remove a cushion each time until there is only one left.

Mouse ears

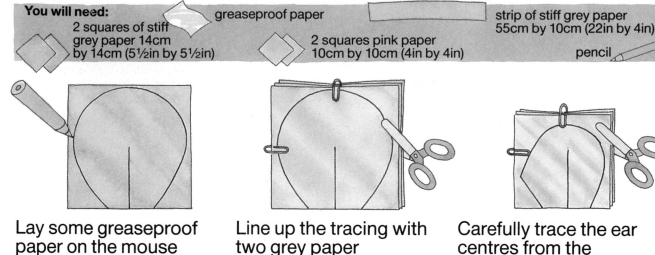

You will need:
2 squares of stiff grey paper 14cm by 14cm (5½in by 5½in)

greaseproof paper

2 squares pink paper 10cm by 10cm (4in by 4in)

strip of stiff grey paper 55cm by 10cm (22in by 4in)

pencil

Lay some greaseproof paper on the mouse ear template*. Trace the outline and centre line with a pencil.

Line up the tracing with two grey paper squares and secure it with paper clips. Cut along all the drawn lines carefully, then remove the tracing.

Carefully trace the ear centres from the template*. Using pink paper, cut them out in the same way as the outer ears.

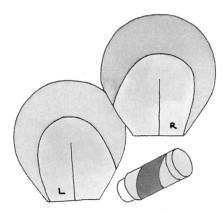

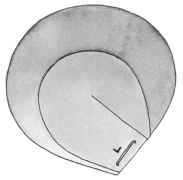

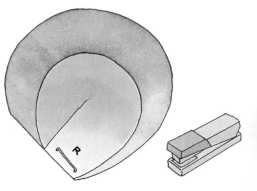

Turn the top ear centre over and glue both centres to the ears, matching corners and centre lines. Label them left and right.

Lift the left side of the left ear and overlap onto the right side. Match the corners and staple, as shown.

Lift the right side of the right ear and overlap onto the left side. Match the corners and staple at the base.

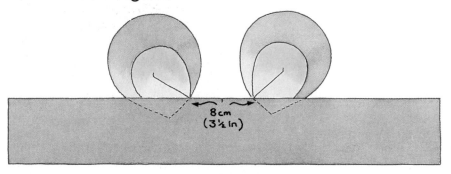

8cm (3½in)

Mark the centre of the paper strip. Staple left and right ears at each side 8cm (3½in) apart.

*See templates on pages 190-191.

round-ended scissors
stapler
sticky tape
glue stick
paper clips
ruler

Fold the band over itself to hide the staples. Fit the band round the head and secure it with paper clips.

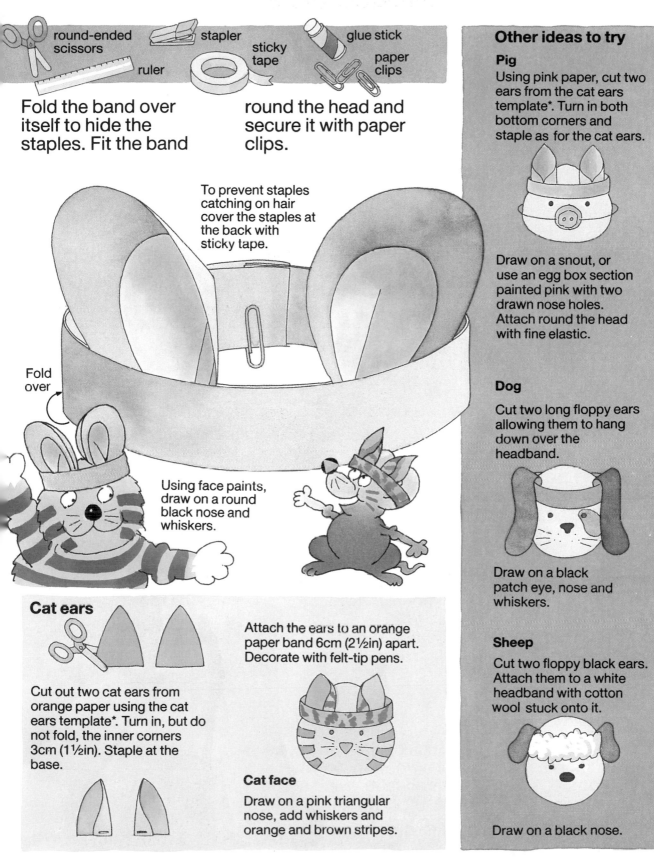

To prevent staples catching on hair cover the staples at the back with sticky tape.

Fold over

Using face paints, draw on a round black nose and whiskers.

Cat ears

Cut out two cat ears from orange paper using the cat ears template*. Turn in, but do not fold, the inner corners 3cm (1½in). Staple at the base.

Attach the ears to an orange paper band 6cm (2½in) apart. Decorate with felt-tip pens.

Cat face

Draw on a pink triangular nose, add whiskers and orange and brown stripes.

Other ideas to try

Pig

Using pink paper, cut two ears from the cat ears template*. Turn in both bottom corners and staple as for the cat ears.

Draw on a snout, or use an egg box section painted pink with two drawn nose holes. Attach round the head with fine elastic.

Dog

Cut two long floppy ears allowing them to hang down over the headband.

Draw on a black patch eye, nose and whiskers.

Sheep

Cut two floppy black ears. Attach them to a white headband with cotton wool stuck onto it.

Draw on a black nose.

175

Pirate fancy dress

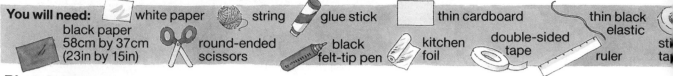
You will need: white paper · string · glue stick · thin cardboard · thin black elastic
black paper 58cm by 37cm (23in by 15in) · round-ended scissors · black felt-tip pen · kitchen foil · double-sided tape · ruler · sti ta

Pirate's hat

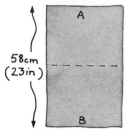

58cm (23in)

Fold the piece of black paper so that edge A meets edge B exactly.

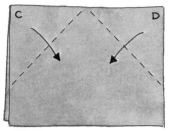

Now fold the points marked C and D so they meet in the centre.

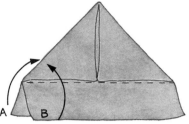

Fold up the edges B and A on either side to complete the hat.

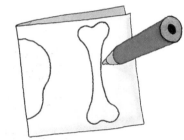

Fold a white piece of paper in half. Draw half a skull and a bone.

Cut out the skull and crossbones. Draw in the skull's face with a black felt-tip pen.

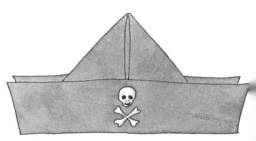

Glue the shapes onto the front of your hat, like this.

Dagger

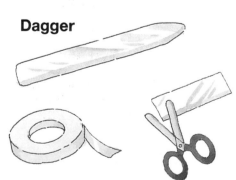

Cut out a rounded blade and handle from thin cardboard. Cover both pieces with kitchen foil using tape.

Stick on the handle, as shown, with double-sided tape. Wind some string round the handle and tape the ends.

Treasure map

Tear round a piece of unlined white paper. Soak in cold tea for a few minutes. Hang it up to dry. Use brown felt-tip pen to draw a treasure map. Roll it up loosely and tie it with a red ribbon.

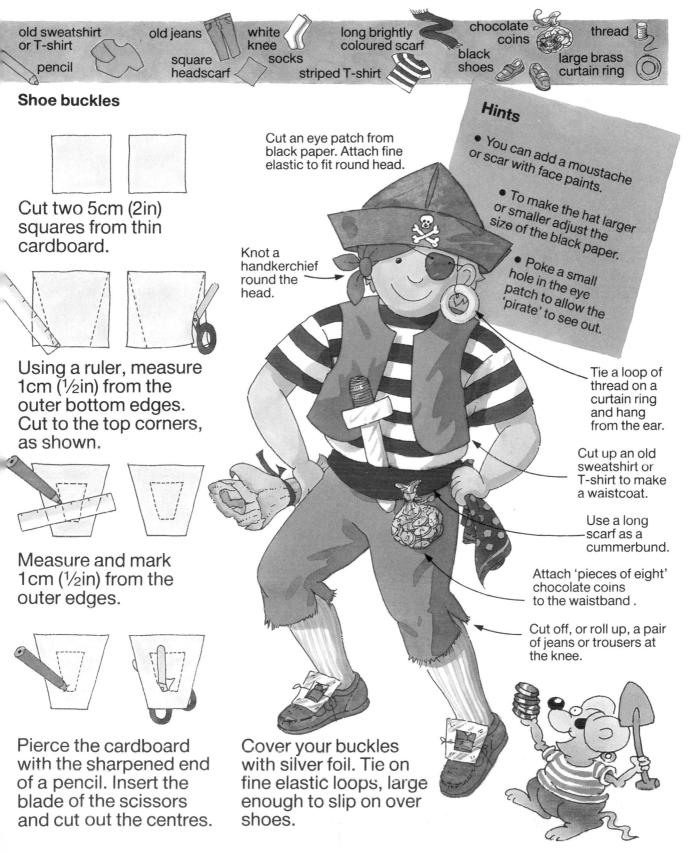

old sweatshirt or T-shirt

pencil

old jeans

square headscarf

white knee socks

striped T-shirt

long brightly coloured scarf

chocolate coins

black shoes

striped T-shirt

thread

large brass curtain ring

Shoe buckles

Cut two 5cm (2in) squares from thin cardboard.

Using a ruler, measure 1cm (½in) from the outer bottom edges. Cut to the top corners, as shown.

Measure and mark 1cm (½in) from the outer edges.

Pierce the cardboard with the sharpened end of a pencil. Insert the blade of the scissors and cut out the centres.

Cut an eye patch from black paper. Attach fine elastic to fit round head.

Knot a handkerchief round the head.

Hints

• You can add a moustache or scar with face paints.

• To make the hat larger or smaller adjust the size of the black paper.

• Poke a small hole in the eye patch to allow the 'pirate' to see out.

Tie a loop of thread on a curtain ring and hang from the ear.

Cut up an old sweatshirt or T-shirt to make a waistcoat.

Use a long scarf as a cummerbund.

Attach 'pieces of eight' chocolate coins to the waistband.

Cut off, or roll up, a pair of jeans or trousers at the knee.

Cover your buckles with silver foil. Tie on fine elastic loops, large enough to slip on over shoes.

177

Little witch

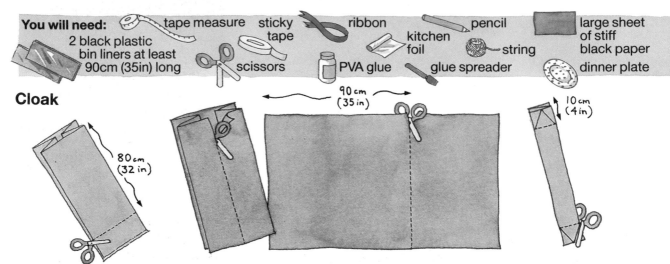

Cloak

With the open end of a bin liner at the top, cut a wide tube 80cm (32in) deep. Keep the remaining piece.

Cut the top layer and open it out to make a wide strip. Trim the strip to 90cm (35in) wide.

Fold the strip in half widthways three times. Cut the top and bottom into points about 10cm (4in) deep.

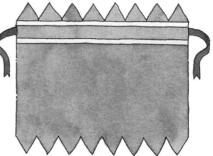

From the remaining piece of bin liner cut a band, as shown, 90cm (35in) long and 8cm (3in) wide.

Open out the folded strip and lay the band over the top of the cloak. Tape along the top edge.

Lay a ribbon between the cloak and the band. Tape down the bottom edge. Draw up the ribbon to gather the neck edge.

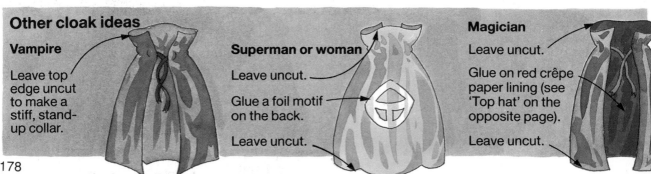

Other cloak ideas

Vampire

Leave top edge uncut to make a stiff, stand-up collar.

Superman or woman

Leave uncut.

Glue a foil motif on the back.

Leave uncut.

Magician

Leave uncut.

Glue on red crêpe paper lining (see 'Top hat' on the opposite page).

Leave uncut.

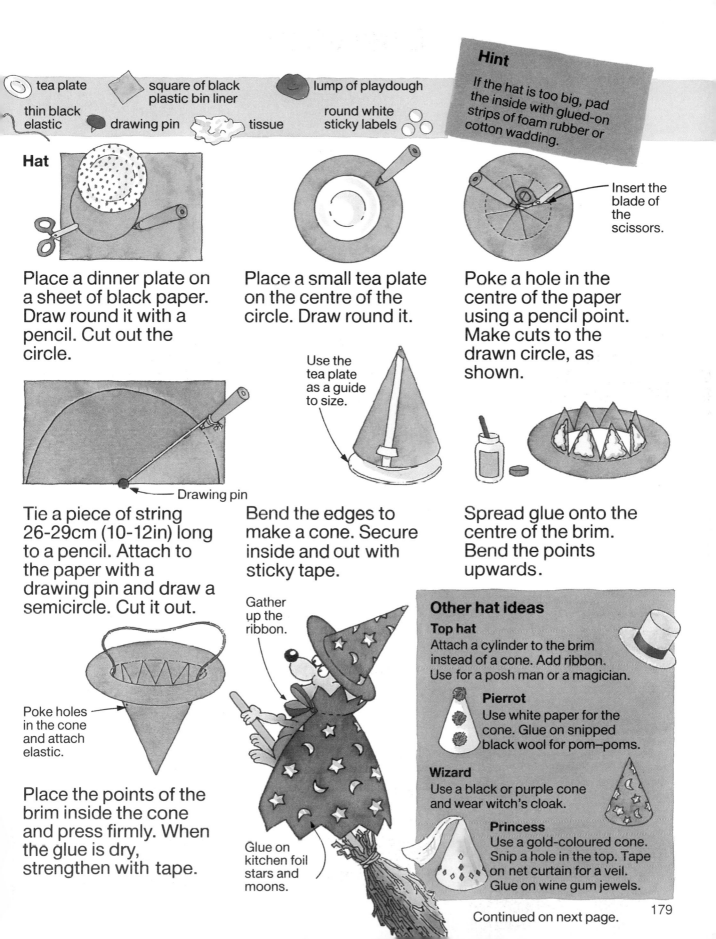

tea plate

square of black plastic bin liner

lump of playdough

thin black elastic

drawing pin

tissue

round white sticky labels

Hint

If the hat is too big, pad the inside with glued-on strips of foam rubber or cotton wadding.

Hat

Place a dinner plate on a sheet of black paper. Draw round it with a pencil. Cut out the circle.

Place a small tea plate on the centre of the circle. Draw round it.

Poke a hole in the centre of the paper using a pencil point. Make cuts to the drawn circle, as shown.

Insert the blade of the scissors.

Use the tea plate as a guide to size.

Tie a piece of string 26-29cm (10-12in) long to a pencil. Attach to the paper with a drawing pin and draw a semicircle. Cut it out.

Drawing pin

Bend the edges to make a cone. Secure inside and out with sticky tape.

Spread glue onto the centre of the brim. Bend the points upwards.

Poke holes in the cone and attach elastic.

Place the points of the brim inside the cone and press firmly. When the glue is dry, strengthen with tape.

Gather up the ribbon.

Glue on kitchen foil stars and moons.

Other hat ideas

Top hat
Attach a cylinder to the brim instead of a cone. Add ribbon. Use for a posh man or a magician.

Pierrot
Use white paper for the cone. Glue on snipped black wool for pom-poms.

Wizard
Use a black or purple cone and wear witch's cloak.

Princess
Use a gold-coloured cone. Snip a hole in the top. Tape on net curtain for a veil. Glue on wine gum jewels.

179

Continued on next page.

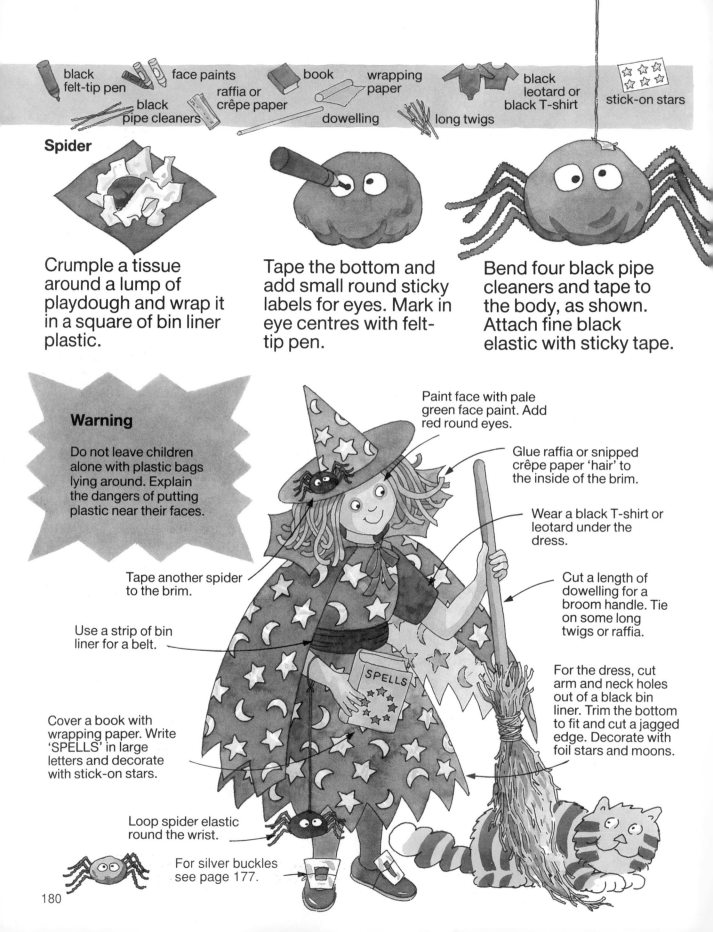

black felt-tip pen

face paints

raffia or crêpe paper

black pipe cleaners

book

wrapping paper

dowelling

long twigs

black leotard or black T-shirt

stick-on stars

Spider

Crumple a tissue around a lump of playdough and wrap it in a square of bin liner plastic.

Tape the bottom and add small round sticky labels for eyes. Mark in eye centres with felt-tip pen.

Bend four black pipe cleaners and tape to the body, as shown. Attach fine black elastic with sticky tape.

Warning

Do not leave children alone with plastic bags lying around. Explain the dangers of putting plastic near their faces.

Paint face with pale green face paint. Add red round eyes.

Glue raffia or snipped crêpe paper 'hair' to the inside of the brim.

Wear a black T-shirt or leotard under the dress.

Tape another spider to the brim.

Cut a length of dowelling for a broom handle. Tie on some long twigs or raffia.

Use a strip of bin liner for a belt.

SPELLS

For the dress, cut arm and neck holes out of a black bin liner. Trim the bottom to fit and cut a jagged edge. Decorate with foil stars and moons.

Cover a book with wrapping paper. Write 'SPELLS' in large letters and decorate with stick-on stars.

Loop spider elastic round the wrist.

For silver buckles see page 177.

180

Other dressing-up ideas

Waitress

Stick half a doily onto a strip of stiff white paper. Secure with paper clips at the back.

Lipstick

Doily 'collar' and 'cuffs'.

Fold a card and stick food pictures inside.

Tape a small and large doily together for the apron. Add a white ribbon.

Tie on a notebook and pencil.

Use a polystyrene pizza base as a tray. Glue on a paper cup with straw. Fill small cake cases with breakfast cereal mixed with PVA glue. Paint the 'cakes' brown and glue onto tray.

Chef

Tape the edges of a circle of white crêpe paper to the inside of a white paper band.

Dust the face with flour.

Apron

Small rolling pin

Pastry brush

Wooden spoon

For the sausages, stuff the legs of old tights and tie at intervals with thread.

Spider

Black balaclava

You can glue on silver foil stripes.

Stuff the legs of old black tights and attach with a safety pin.

Black gloves

Black jumper

Suspend 'legs' from strong black thread.

Black tights

Black plimsolls

Clown

Slippers

Cut-down too-large trousers.

Cotton patches

Braces

For the buttons, cut off the bottoms of paper cups. Poke in holes and sew lightly onto T-shirt.

Scarf 'bow-tie'

Nose made of an egg carton section painted red. Tie on with elastic.

Rubber bands keep gloves on.

181

Fishing game

You will need: pencil · plastic straws · brightly coloured tissue paper · sticky tape · large sheet of blue tissue paper · thin string · paper plates · thin wrapping paper

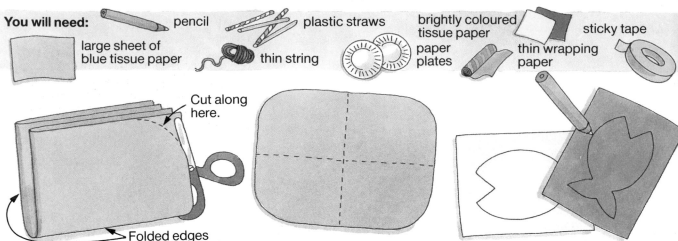

Cut along here.

Folded edges

Fold a sheet of blue tissue paper into four. Round off the outer corner with scissors, as shown.

Open it and smooth it out on the floor. This is your pond.

On pieces of tissue paper and wrapping paper draw large, simple fish shapes about 15cm (6in) long. You will need 15 to 20 fishes.

Hints

- Use thin wrapping paper or the magnet won't pick up the fish.

- Cut out a number of fish at a time by cutting through several layers of paper.

- Adjust the rod according to the height of the child by winding or unwinding the string round the straw.

- To store the game wind the string round each straw and fold the pond. Keep all the pieces in a flat box.

Cut out the shapes neatly. Decorate your fish with felt-tip pens.

Turn the fish shapes over. Place a paper clip near the mouth of each fish. Secure the paper clips with sticky tape.

Flapping fish game

Cut out large tissue paper fish shapes about 25cm (10in) long. Decorate them with felt-tip pens. Race your fish by blowing them or flapping them with rolled-up newspaper. Use a wool strand as a starting line.

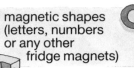

magnetic shapes (letters, numbers or any other fridge magnets)

round-ended scissors

felt-tip pens

metal paper clips

Take-home fish

Draw a fat fish shape, about 20cm (8in) long, on tissue paper. Spread glue thickly round the edges using glue stick. Place small flat sweets in the centre, away from the glued edges.

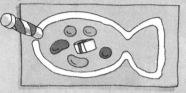

To make a fishing rod, tie one end of a piece of string round a magnetic shape.

Tie the other end of the string onto the end of a straw. Use sticky tape to prevent the string slipping. Make a rod for each of your party guests.

Lay a second piece of tissue over the fish. Press the edges down firmly. Neatly cut the fish shape out.

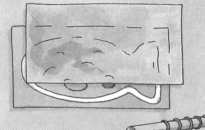

Stick on a paper reinforcement ring, as shown. Pierce the centre of the ring with the sharpened end of a pencil. Thread a piece of string through the hole and knot it. Tie the other end to a straw 'rod'. Write the child's name at the bottom.

Harry

Arrange the fish on the pond. Give all the players a paper plate on which to land their 'catch'.

Buzzing bees game

Flowers

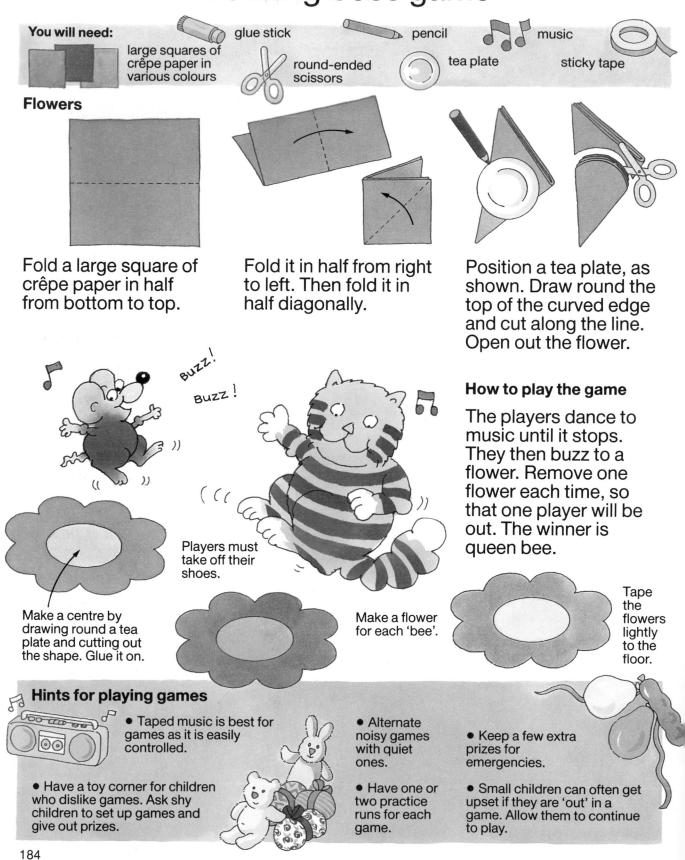

Fold a large square of crêpe paper in half from bottom to top.

Fold it in half from right to left. Then fold it in half diagonally.

Position a tea plate, as shown. Draw round the top of the curved edge and cut along the line. Open out the flower.

BUZZ!

BUZZ!

Players must take off their shoes.

How to play the game

The players dance to music until it stops. They then buzz to a flower. Remove one flower each time, so that one player will be out. The winner is queen bee.

Make a centre by drawing round a tea plate and cutting out the shape. Glue it on.

Make a flower for each 'bee'.

Tape the flowers lightly to the floor.

Hints for playing games

- Taped music is best for games as it is easily controlled.

- Have a toy corner for children who dislike games. Ask shy children to set up games and give out prizes.

- Alternate noisy games with quiet ones.

- Have one or two practice runs for each game.

- Keep a few extra prizes for emergencies.

- Small children can often get upset if they are 'out' in a game. Allow them to continue to play.

Poor piggy

Piggy

Tie rubber bands round two corners of the pillowcase. Draw on eyes and a snout with pink felt-tip pen or paint.

Fit a pillow inside the pillowcase. Gather in the 'neck' with a wide ribbon

How to play the game

Pass poor piggy round in a circle until the music stops. Whoever is holding poor piggy calls out 'oink oink' and collects a prize from the bowl in the centre.

Hint

Make sure the person in charge of the music can see all the players clearly so that every child 'wins' a prize.

Other games to play

Adapt the buzzing bees game for a theme party. Cut out islands for pirates to jump on, or honey pots for teddy bears.

Wool gathering

Players find pieces of wool hidden round a room while music plays. When the music stops, the child with most pieces gives out a sweet 'prize' to the others.

Chocolate egg race

Small chocolate eggs, placed in a plastic bowl, are scooped up with plastic teaspoons and raced to woolly hat nests. When the music stops, the nest with most eggs wins. This can be a team game.

Ping-pong ball race

Using straws, race ping-pong balls by blowing them along the floor into an upturned box 'goal'. No hands allowed.

Miming games

One player mimes an animal while the others guess. Try other themes, such as circus performers or sports.

185

Outdoor party fun

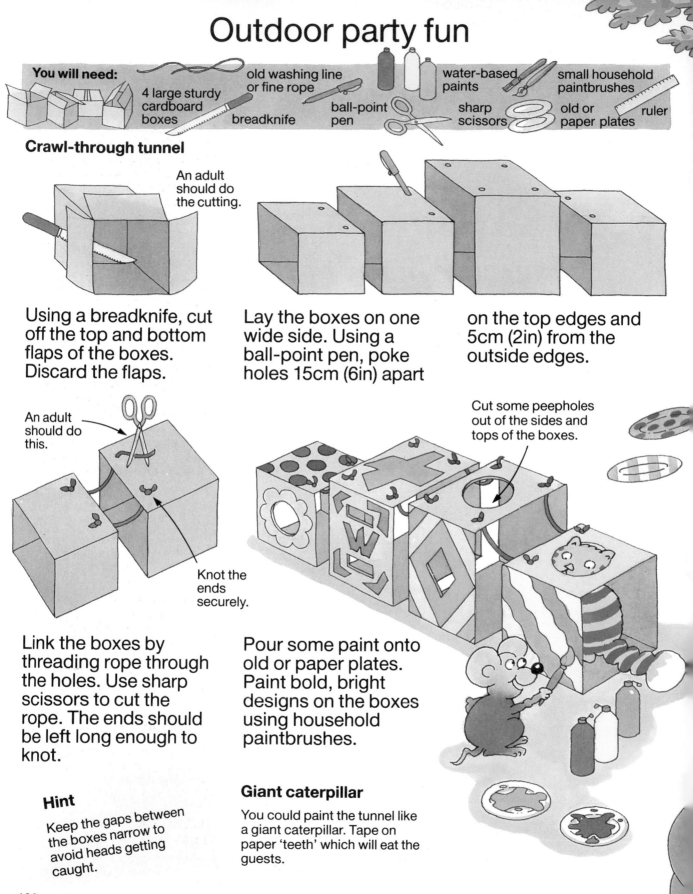

Crawl-through tunnel

An adult should do the cutting.

Using a breadknife, cut off the top and bottom flaps of the boxes. Discard the flaps.

Lay the boxes on one wide side. Using a ball-point pen, poke holes 15cm (6in) apart

on the top edges and 5cm (2in) from the outside edges.

An adult should do this.

Knot the ends securely.

Cut some peepholes out of the sides and tops of the boxes.

Link the boxes by threading rope through the holes. Use sharp scissors to cut the rope. The ends should be left long enough to knot.

Pour some paint onto old or paper plates. Paint bold, bright designs on the boxes using household paintbrushes.

Hint

Keep the gaps between the boxes narrow to avoid heads getting caught.

Giant caterpillar

You could paint the tunnel like a giant caterpillar. Tape on paper 'teeth' which will eat the guests.

186

Other ideas

Washing line

Old sheet

Tent

Knot corners to safe tent pegs.

Playhouse

Make from old fridge or cooker box.

Frisbees

Decorate paper plates.

Bubble blowing

One part soap liquid to two parts water

Washing basket game

Rolled sock

Fishing game

Hard-boiled egg hunt

Buckets for the 'catch'

Tunnel

Some theme party ideas

Colour party

Choose a colour, for example yellow. Make yellow invitations, asking your guests to wear yellow. The table decor and food should include as much yellow as possible.

Give yellow balloons as gifts and prizes. Play the wool game using yellow wool (see page 185), make a yellow fish game (see page 182).

Animal party

Ask your guests to wear animal costume. Play 'animal freeze', by calling out the names of animals which children become before freezing. Give animal pencil-top prizes (see page 164). Play 'Poor piggy' and 'Buzzing bees' (see pages 184-185).

Christmas party

Send 'potato print snowman' invitations. Tape tinsel garlands round a red or green crêpe paper tablecloth.

Hide a small wrapped present and play 'Hunt the present'. Make a chimney lucky dip (see page 188).

Clown party

Everyone dresses as clowns (see page 181). Stick a balloon onto the invitations. Make 'balloon people' and 'balloon clown' pictures (see pages 166-7).

Mice and cheese lucky dip

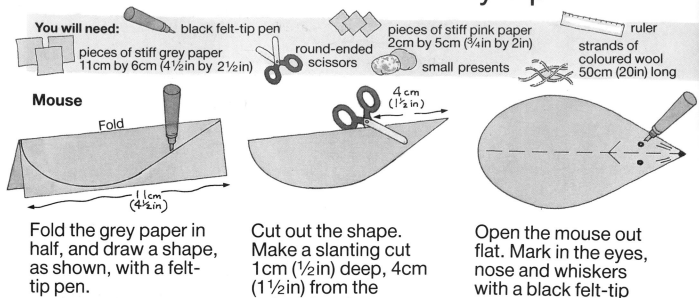

Mouse

Fold the grey paper in half, and draw a shape, as shown, with a felt-tip pen.

Cut out the shape. Make a slanting cut 1cm (½in) deep, 4cm (1½in) from the pointed end.

Open the mouse out flat. Mark in the eyes, nose and whiskers with a black felt-tip pen.

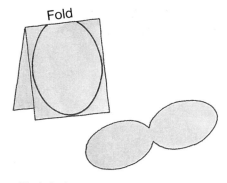

Fold the pink paper, as shown. Draw and cut out the ears, leaving them joined at the fold.

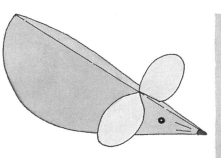

Fold the mouse again and stand it upright. Then slot the ears into the cut on the mouse's back.

Other ideas

Make a Christmas chimney pot. Cut the flaps off a tall box and cover it with brown paper. Paint or, using a sponge, print red bricks. Glue on cotton wool snow and sprinkle with glitter.

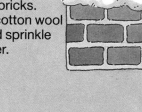

For very young children, cover a large box with bright paper. Fill with wrapped presents mixed among lots of small soft toys.

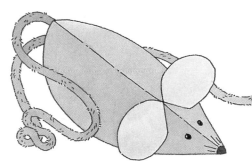

Tape one end of the wool to the inside top of the mouse's body.

Tape a small wrapped present to the other end of the wool. Make one mouse per guest.

Wrap a large box to look like a parcel. Paint on a stamp. Cut a hole in the side and fill it with presents.

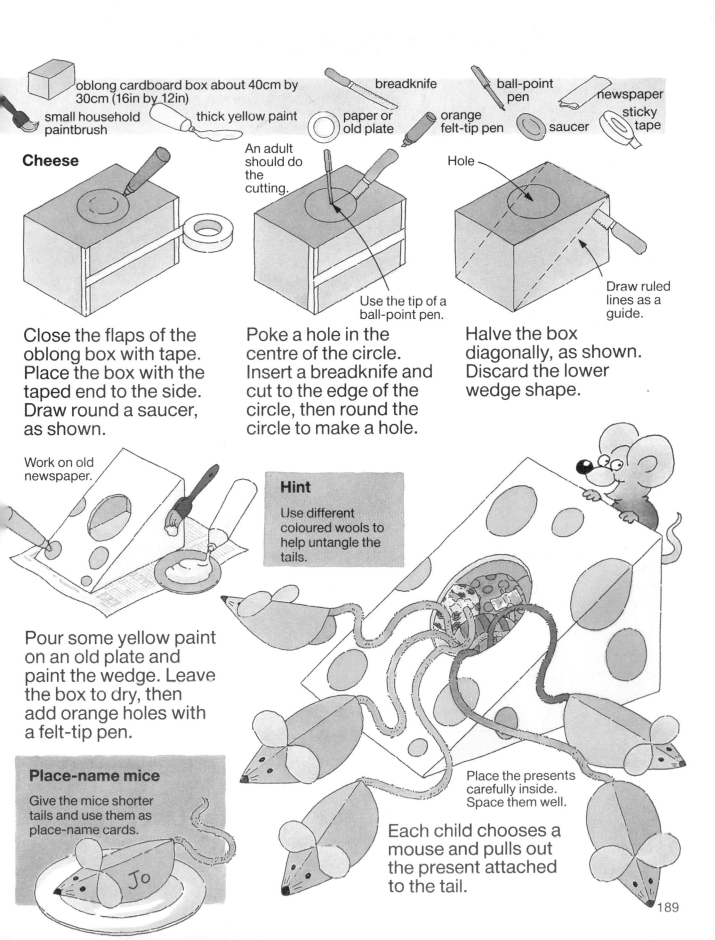

oblong cardboard box about 40cm by 30cm (16in by 12in)

breadknife

ball-point pen

newspaper

small household paintbrush

thick yellow paint

paper or old plate

orange felt-tip pen

saucer

sticky tape

Cheese

An adult should do the cutting.

Hole

Use the tip of a ball-point pen.

Draw ruled lines as a guide.

Close the flaps of the oblong box with tape. Place the box with the taped end to the side. Draw round a saucer, as shown.

Poke a hole in the centre of the circle. Insert a breadknife and cut to the edge of the circle, then round the circle to make a hole.

Halve the box diagonally, as shown. Discard the lower wedge shape.

Work on old newspaper.

Hint

Use different coloured wools to help untangle the tails.

Pour some yellow paint on an old plate and paint the wedge. Leave the box to dry, then add orange holes with a felt-tip pen.

Place-name mice

Give the mice shorter tails and use them as place-name cards.

Jo

Place the presents carefully inside. Space them well.

Each child chooses a mouse and pulls out the present attached to the tail.

189

Templates

Pencil-top templates

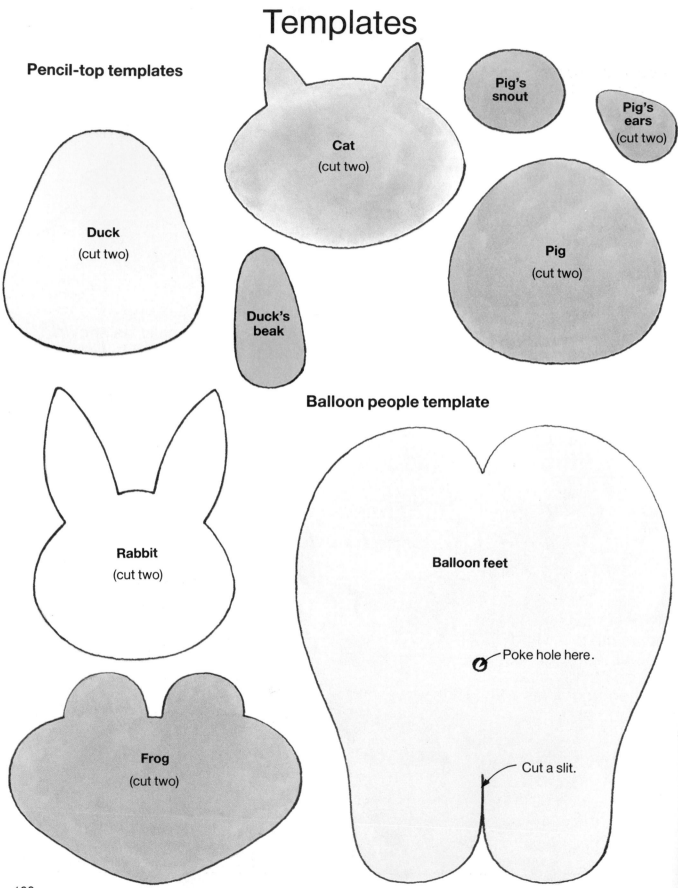

Duck
(cut two)

Cat
(cut two)

Pig's snout

Pig's ears
(cut two)

Pig
(cut two)

Duck's beak

Balloon people template

Rabbit
(cut two)

Frog
(cut two)

Balloon feet

Poke hole here.

Cut a slit.

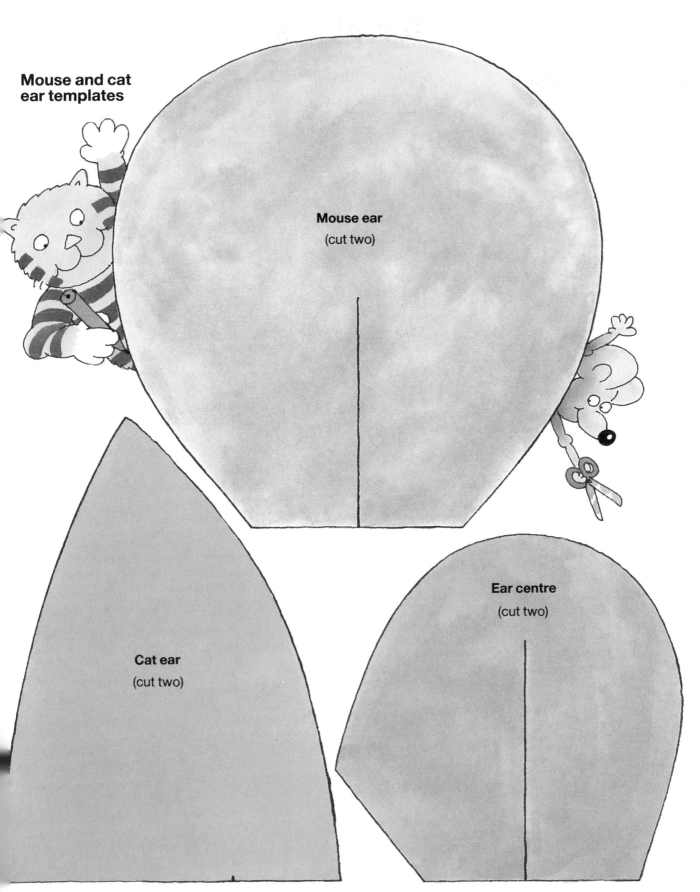

Mouse and cat ear templates

Mouse ear
(cut two)

Cat ear
(cut two)

Ear centre
(cut two)

Party hints

Number of guests

Large numbers of people can overwhelm small children, especially if they are unfamiliar with all the guests and adults present. A small number of close friends can often work better. If there are more than one or two 'new' children, it can be a good idea to provide name badges. These could be sent with the party invitations.

Games

If you have room, provide a selection of toys in a small corner for children who find it difficult joining in games. Shy children can also be encouraged to hand out sweets or prizes, and help to set up the games.

Alternate noisy games with quiet ones and end the party with a 'keeping still' or 'lying on the floor' game.

Safety

It is important to make sure the party area is safe. Make sure that outside gates are secure and that rooms you wish to be undisturbed are locked and keys removed. These places could act as stores for delicate or dangerous objects, or furniture which has been cleared to create space.

Make sure outside ponds or paddling pools are drained or covered, and garden tools are locked away. Have a small first-aid kit handy.

Food

Don't make food too elaborate, except, perhaps, for a birthday cake which your child may like to help you make.

You can avoid 'one bite' leftovers by keeping the food small. Bowls of finger foods, such as crisps and cut-up sausages; tiny sandwiches and small cakes in petit four cases make ideal party fare. You could also provide individual juice cartons to avoid spills.

Materials

The specific things you will need for each project are listed at the top of each page. Below is some general advice on equipment and materials.

Scissors should be round-ended. If sharp ones are needed remember to place them safely out of reach. Cut roughly round the shape you want and then it will be easier to neaten the cut edge.

Paper. Packs of coloured play paper can be bought quite cheaply. You can also use wrapping paper or wallpaper but make sure it is a suitable thickness for your project. Breakfast cereal boxes make a good source of thin cardboard.

Glue sticks are clean to use, and they do not cause wrinkling on thin paper such as tissue.

PVA (polyvinyl acetate) glue is good for large areas. It is white but dries transparent. It can be used to thicken water-based paint. Protect clothing and wash brushes after use.

Wallpaper paste makes a good glue for large areas. For safety, use the non-fungicidal kind.

Tube glue should be non-toxic. Do not use instant-bond or solvent based glues.

Sticky tape. It is best to cut several lengths at once and attach lightly to a work surface edge for easy use.

Magnetic shapes are available from large stationers and shops stocking educational toys. They can often be bought as alphabet letters or numbers.

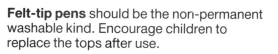

Felt-tip pens should be the non-permanent washable kind. Encourage children to replace the tops after use.

Glitter should be used with care. Avoid rubbing eyes during use and wash hands afterwards. Tip any excess into the fold of a magazine and pour back into the container.

Knives should be plastic, or round-ended kitchen knives.

Paintbrushes. Use small household paintbrushes for painting large areas. Use children's paintbrushes for finer patterns.

YOU AND YOUR CHILD
CHRISTMAS

Much of the pleasure of Christmas is in the anticipation and preparation. This book provides parents and children with lots of ideas for simple things to make together to get themselves in the festive mood. There are hanging decorations, table decorations and tree decorations; ideas for advent calendars, cards and presents and tasty things to eat. Besides introducing children to some Christmas traditions and helping them to play a part in the preparations, the activities in this book provide the context for a wealth of learning opportunities.

Christmas angel

You will need:
1 large doily
round-ended scissors
stiff red paper
scrap of pink paper
yellow wool
sticky tape
cotton wool
paper clip
PVA glue
glue stick

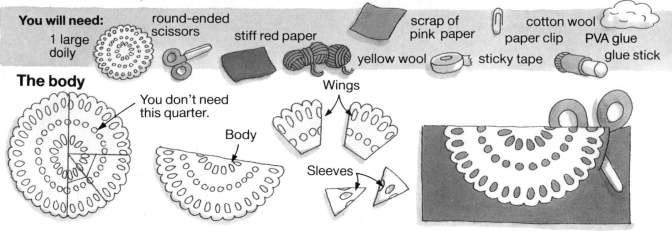

The body

You don't need this quarter.

Wings

Body

Sleeves

Draw lines on the doily, as shown above. Cut along them to make two wings, sleeves and a body.

Spread glue on the back of the body piece and stick it onto red paper. When dry, cut around the edge of the doily.

On the back, glue along half of the straight edge.

Snip across the top to leave a small hole.

Hold in place with a paper clip until it is dry.

Bend it into a cone shape, overlapping the glued edge and press it down firmly.

Fold a piece of pink paper and cut out two small hands.
   Glue them onto the ends of the sleeves. Leave them to dry.

Other ideas to try

Wise men

Instead of haloes give them kitchen paper headdresses.

Fairy

Give her a tinsel headdress and glue sequins over her dress and wings.

Angel mobile

Make several angels and hang them from a garden cane.

The join goes down the back of the body.

Glue the pointed end of the sleeves to the body, as shown.

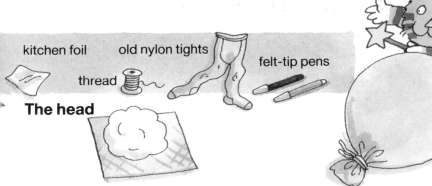

kitchen foil   old nylon tights

thread   felt-tip pens

The head

Tease out some cotton wool and roll it into a firm ball. Put it in the centre of a square cut from some nylon tights.

Gather the nylon around the cotton wool, twist the corners together and tie thread around them.

Draw on some eyes, a nose and a mouth with felt-tip pen.

Snip some wool into short pieces for hair. Put glue onto the head and press them on.

Push the bottom of the head firmly through the hole in the top of the cone. Fix it inside with sticky tape.

Cut out a circle of foil and glue it onto the back of the head as a halo.

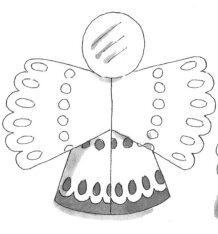

Glue the wings to the back of the body, over the arms and hands.

Hint

• To make the wings really strong, you could stick them onto clear cellophane, before attaching them to the body.

Swedish hanging biscuits

You will need:
- 225 g (8 oz) plain flour
- 115 g (4 oz) margarine
- ½ teaspoon bicarbonate of soda
- pinch of ground cloves
- ¾ teaspoon cinnamon
- icing sugar
- 115 g (4 oz) dark brown sugar
- green and red glacé cherries
- 1 egg white
- ¾ teaspoon ground ginger
- cold water

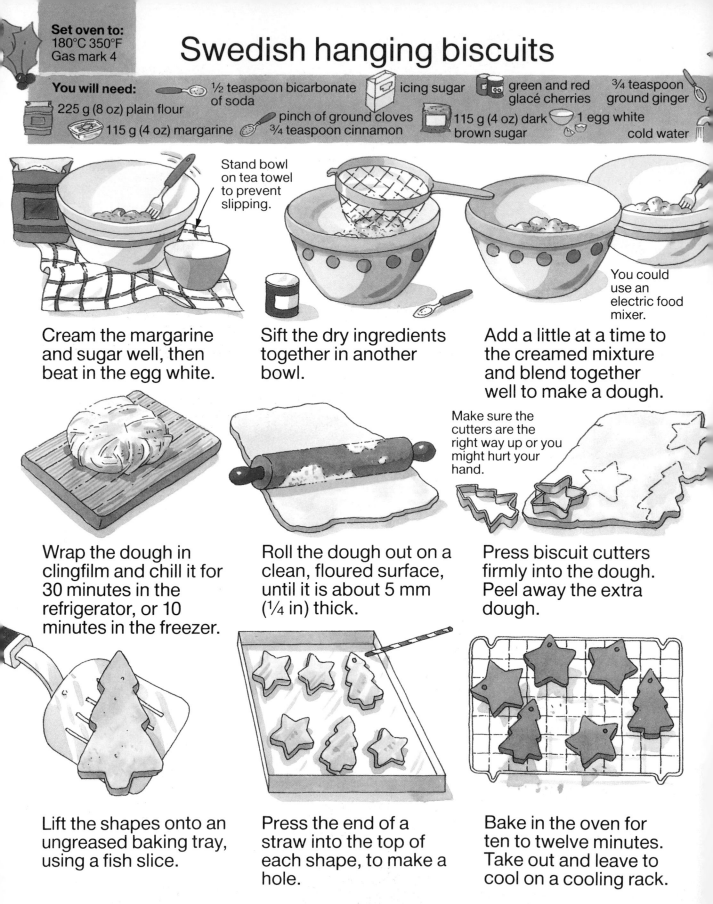

Stand bowl on tea towel to prevent slipping.

Cream the margarine and sugar well, then beat in the egg white.

Sift the dry ingredients together in another bowl.

You could use an electric food mixer.

Add a little at a time to the creamed mixture and blend together well to make a dough.

Wrap the dough in clingfilm and chill it for 30 minutes in the refrigerator, or 10 minutes in the freezer.

Roll the dough out on a clean, floured surface, until it is about 5 mm (¼ in) thick.

Make sure the cutters are the right way up or you might hurt your hand.

Press biscuit cutters firmly into the dough. Peel away the extra dough.

Lift the shapes onto an ungreased baking tray, using a fish slice.

Press the end of a straw into the top of each shape, to make a hole.

Bake in the oven for ten to twelve minutes. Take out and leave to cool on a cooling rack.

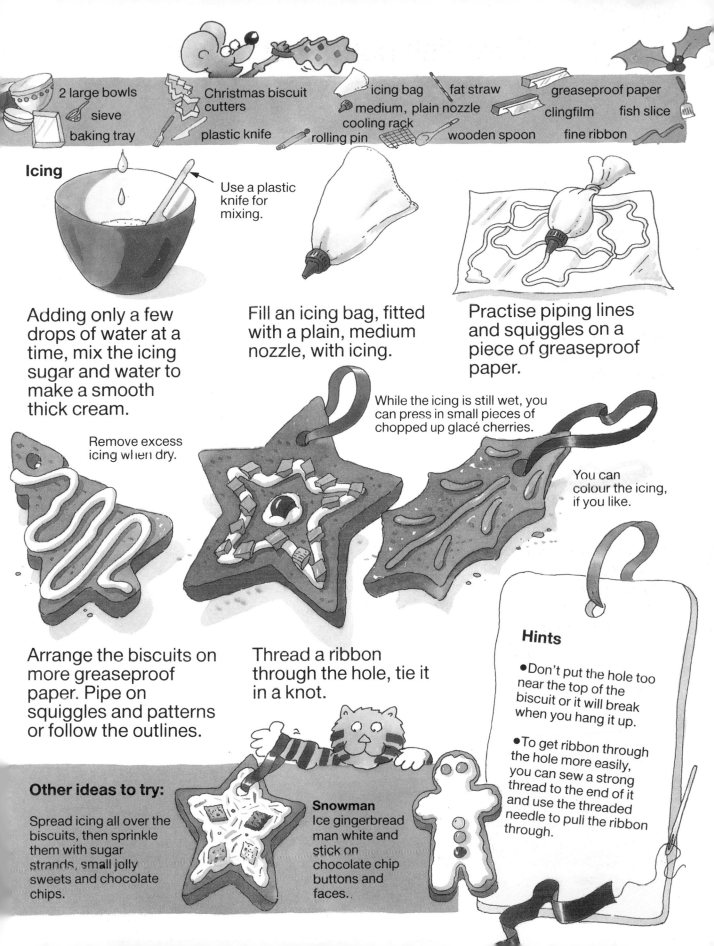

2 large bowls
sieve
baking tray
Christmas biscuit cutters
plastic knife
icing bag
medium, plain nozzle
cooling rack
rolling pin
fat straw
wooden spoon
greaseproof paper
clingfilm   fish slice
fine ribbon

Icing

Use a plastic knife for mixing.

Adding only a few drops of water at a time, mix the icing sugar and water to make a smooth thick cream.

Fill an icing bag, fitted with a plain, medium nozzle, with icing.

Practise piping lines and squiggles on a piece of greaseproof paper.

Remove excess icing when dry.

While the icing is still wet, you can press in small pieces of chopped up glacé cherries.

You can colour the icing, if you like.

Arrange the biscuits on more greaseproof paper. Pipe on squiggles and patterns or follow the outlines.

Thread a ribbon through the hole, tie it in a knot.

Hints

• Don't put the hole too near the top of the biscuit or it will break when you hang it up.

• To get ribbon through the hole more easily, you can sew a strong thread to the end of it and use the threaded needle to pull the ribbon through.

Other ideas to try:

Spread icing all over the biscuits, then sprinkle them with sugar strands, small jolly sweets and chocolate chips.

Snowman
Ice gingerbread man white and stick on chocolate chip buttons and faces.

Glitter garlands

You will need: wool · glitter (several different colours) · mug · non-solvent glue and brush · tapestry needle · coloured bendy straws · round-ended scissors · old magazine

Open an old magazine out flat and pour glitter in a line down the centre fold.

Bend the short end of a straw and using it as a handle brush glue all over the long end.

Roll the straw in the glitter until it is covered. Stand it handle end up in a mug to dry.

Repeat this with several more straws.

Tip any excess glitter back into the container.

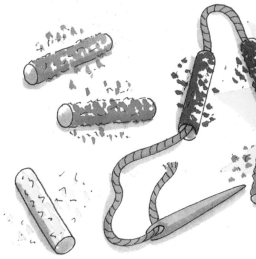

Snip the straws into pieces about 2 or 3 cm (1 in) long. Thread wool through them, using a blunt needle.

Secure the first 'bead' with a knot before continuing.

Hang in loops round the Christmas tree.

Warning

Take care to wash hands immediately after using glitter to avoid it going in eyes and mouths.

Other ideas

Instead of using glitter, wrap straws in strips of kitchen foil.

Secure the foil with sticky tape before snipping the straws.

Cut longer pieces and thread them three at a time to make triangle shapes, tying the ends together at the top.

Paper stockings

You will need: non-solvent glue, round-ended scissors, scraps of tinsel, ribbon, small sweets, strong, bright Christmas paper, paper clips, gift wrap tape, ruler, felt-tip pens

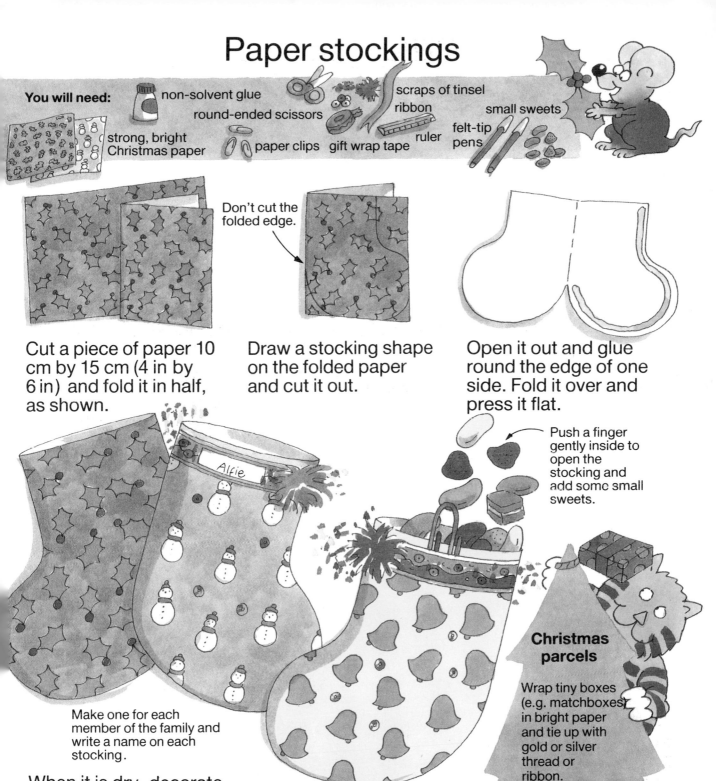

Don't cut the folded edge.

Cut a piece of paper 10 cm by 15 cm (4 in by 6 in) and fold it in half, as shown.

Draw a stocking shape on the folded paper and cut it out.

Open it out and glue round the edge of one side. Fold it over and press it flat.

Push a finger gently inside to open the stocking and add some small sweets.

Make one for each member of the family and write a name on each stocking.

When it is dry, decorate it with Christmas sticky tape and scraps of tinsel.
You could also use stick-on stars, sequins or scraps of tinfoil.

Fix a paperclip to the back with sticky tape, and thread ribbon through and hang it from the Christmas tree.

Christmas parcels

Wrap tiny boxes (e.g. matchboxes) in bright paper and tie up with gold or silver thread or ribbon.

Tape a wool loop to one corner at the back.

Alfie

Candle in a pot

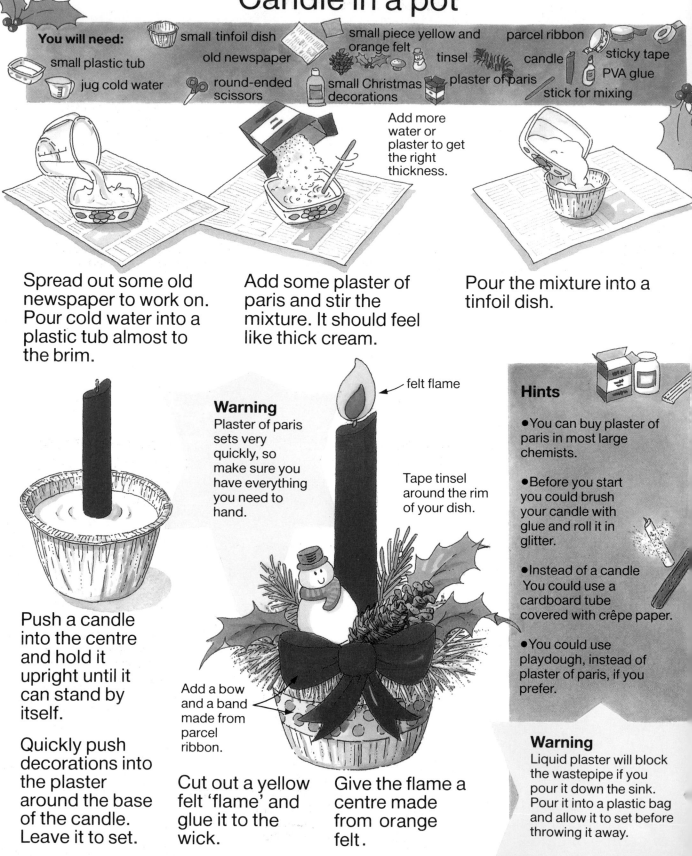

You will need: small plastic tub, small tinfoil dish, old newspaper, small piece yellow and orange felt, parcel ribbon, tinsel, candle, sticky tape, PVA glue, jug cold water, round-ended scissors, small Christmas decorations, plaster of paris, stick for mixing

Add more water or plaster to get the right thickness.

Spread out some old newspaper to work on. Pour cold water into a plastic tub almost to the brim.

Add some plaster of paris and stir the mixture. It should feel like thick cream.

Pour the mixture into a tinfoil dish.

Push a candle into the centre and hold it upright until it can stand by itself.

Quickly push decorations into the plaster around the base of the candle. Leave it to set.

Warning
Plaster of paris sets very quickly, so make sure you have everything you need to hand.

felt flame

Tape tinsel around the rim of your dish.

Add a bow and a band made from parcel ribbon.

Cut out a yellow felt 'flame' and glue it to the wick.

Give the flame a centre made from orange felt.

Hints

• You can buy plaster of paris in most large chemists.

• Before you start you could brush your candle with glue and roll it in glitter.

• Instead of a candle you could use a cardboard tube covered with crêpe paper.

• You could use playdough, instead of plaster of paris, if you prefer.

Warning
Liquid plaster will block the wastepipe if you pour it down the sink. Pour it into a plastic bag and allow it to set before throwing it away.

Robin on a log

You will need: tissue paper: round-ended scissors, 2 sheets brown, small piece red, small piece black, 1 sheet any colour, piece of log, yellow straw, 2 paper plates, holly and berries, pencil, spoon, PVA glue, plaster of paris, water

Cut a double layer of brown tissue paper 17 cm by 17 cm (7 in by 7 in).

Crumple a sheet of tissue to make a fat ball and place it in the centre.

Fix it with sticky tape if necessary.

Gather the edges of the brown tissue paper and twist them into a tail.

Cut the end of a yellow straw to make a point. Trim to 1 cm (½ in).

Using a pencil, poke a hole and push the beak in firmly.

Glue on some eyes made from screwed up black tissue.

Use red paint, or glue on torn red tissue for the breast.

Mix up some plaster of paris* and spoon it thickly over the top of a log to make it look like snow.
   Press the robin into the snow.

You could add some tissue paper wings.

Give him some tiny feet cut from paper.

Stop the log rolling by securing with playdough or setting in plaster.

Snowy mountains

Spoon thick plaster onto a paper plate to make a mound.

Quickly press in plastic foliage and Christmas cake decorations and leave the plaster to dry.

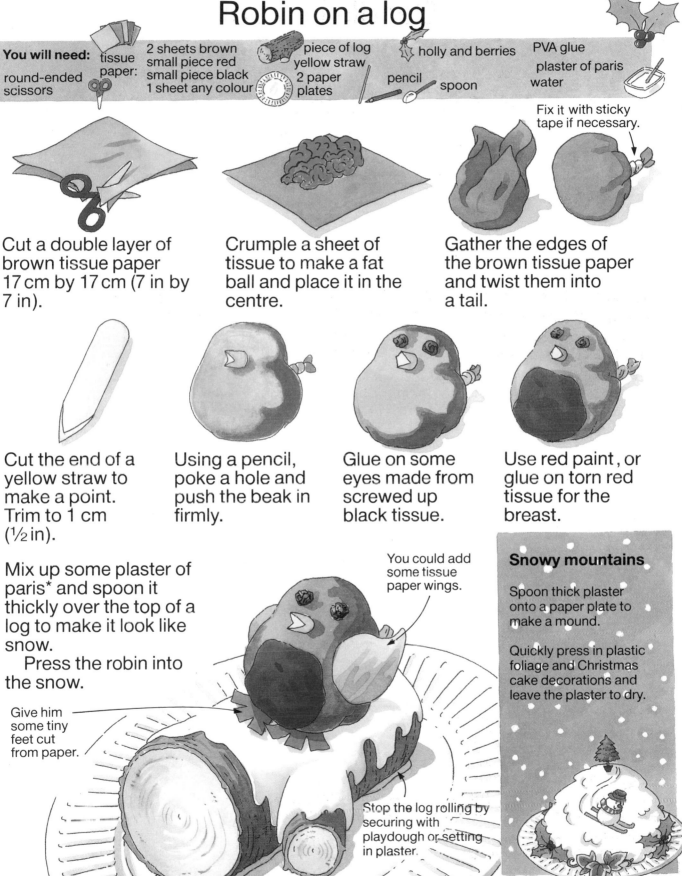

*See opposite page.

Marzipan fun

You will need:

100 g (4 oz) sifted icing sugar

small jug

large mixing bowl

wooden spoon

100 g (4 oz) ground almonds

two teaspoonfuls of lemon juice

1 egg white (see hints)

plastic bag

Making marzipan

Mix the icing sugar and ground almonds together in a mixing bowl, using a wooden spoon.

Beat the lemon juice and egg white together in a small jug, using a fork.

Add half the liquid to the bowl and mix well. Gradually add enough of the remaining liquid to turn the mixture into a stiff paste. Knead until smooth.

Hints

• The texture improves if it is kept in the refrigerator overnight.

• You can buy dried egg white, if you are worried about using uncooked egg white.

• A tea towel placed under the mixing bowl will help to prevent it slipping.

• If you want very strong colours you can paint food colour directly onto the marzipan, using a small brush. Leave it to dry.

Storing

Place in a polythene food bag and keep in the refrigerator. Use within seven days.

Adding colour

Pour drops of colour into small bowls and knead balls of marzipan in them until evenly coloured.

If the marzipan becomes too soft, add more icing sugar and mix well.

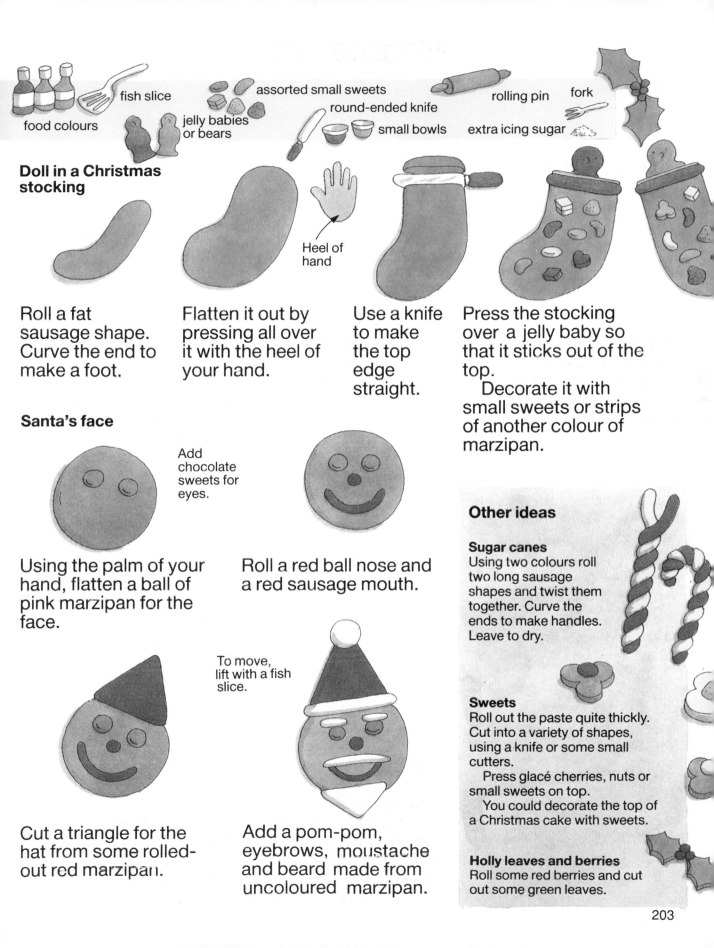

food colours • fish slice • jelly babies or bears • assorted small sweets • round-ended knife • small bowls • rolling pin • extra icing sugar • fork

Doll in a Christmas stocking

Roll a fat sausage shape. Curve the end to make a foot.

Flatten it out by pressing all over it with the heel of your hand.

Heel of hand

Use a knife to make the top edge straight.

Press the stocking over a jelly baby so that it sticks out of the top.

Decorate it with small sweets or strips of another colour of marzipan.

Santa's face

Add chocolate sweets for eyes.

Using the palm of your hand, flatten a ball of pink marzipan for the face.

Roll a red ball nose and a red sausage mouth.

To move, lift with a fish slice.

Cut a triangle for the hat from some rolled-out red marzipan.

Add a pom-pom, eyebrows, moustache and beard made from uncoloured marzipan.

Other ideas

Sugar canes
Using two colours roll two long sausage shapes and twist them together. Curve the ends to make handles. Leave to dry.

Sweets
Roll out the paste quite thickly. Cut into a variety of shapes, using a knife or some small cutters.

Press glacé cherries, nuts or small sweets on top.

You could decorate the top of a Christmas cake with sweets.

Holly leaves and berries
Roll some red berries and cut out some green leaves.

203

Mincemeat

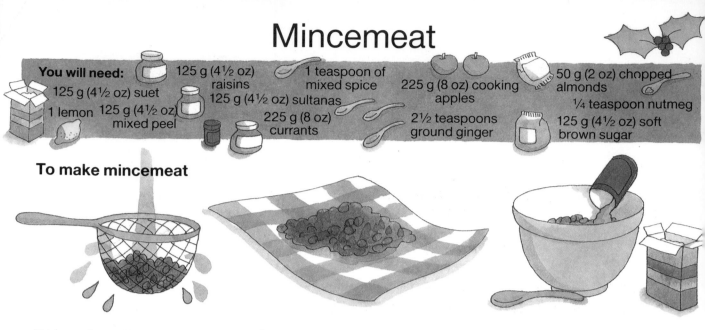

You will need:
- 125 g (4½ oz) suet
- 1 lemon
- 125 g (4½ oz) mixed peel
- 125 g (4½ oz) raisins
- 125 g (4½ oz) sultanas
- 225 g (8 oz) currants
- 1 teaspoon of mixed spice
- 2½ teaspoons ground ginger
- 225 g (8 oz) cooking apples
- 50 g (2 oz) chopped almonds
- ¼ teaspoon nutmeg
- 125 g (4½ oz) soft brown sugar

To make mincemeat

Place the currants, raisins and sultanas in a sieve and wash them under the cold tap.

Shake the sieve well, then tip them onto a clean tea towel and pat them dry.

Tip them into a large bowl. Add sugar, spices, almonds, mixed peel and suet.

Cut the apples into halves, then quarters, then smaller segments.

Cut the peel from each segment and slice out the core from the centres.

You could use a food processor.

Put a few segments at a time onto a chopping board and chop them up finely. Add the apple to the dried fruit.

Wash the lemon and dry it with a tea towel.

With a fine grater, gently grate off the outer rind into a small bowl.

Cut the lemon in half and squeeze out all the juice.

Add the juice and rind to the large bowl.

Mix it up well using a wooden spoon. Leave the mixture covered for 24 hours.

For vegetarians use vegetable suet.

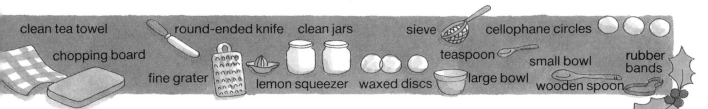

clean tea towel · round-ended knife · clean jars · sieve · cellophane circles
chopping board · fine grater · lemon squeezer · waxed discs · teaspoon · small bowl · rubber bands · large bowl · wooden spoon

To bottle

First you need to sterilize some jam jars by washing them in a dishwasher or using sterilizing solution (see Hint box) .

Fill the jars with mincemeat then place a waxed disc on top. Cover either with a screw top or with a cellophane circle secured with a rubber band.

Leave for at least two weeks before using.

Hint

• You can buy sterilizing solution from chemists. To use it follow the instructions on the bottle or packet.

To mum Love from Carol x

If you want to gift wrap your mincemeat cut a circle of Christmas paper to cover the cellophane. Hold it in place with a ribbon. Stick on a gummed Christmas label.

Merry Christmas

Sadie

Mincemeat munchies

Christmas stars

Using a large star-shaped cutter, cut star shapes from rolled out shortcrust pastry about 3 mm (⅛ in) thick.

Place a little mincemeat in the centre of a star. Brush the edges of the pastry with milk. Place a second star on top to seal it. Glaze with a whole beaten egg.

To decorate snip the top of the pastry with scissors.

Bake on a greased tray at GM 6, 200°C, 400°F for about 15 minutes.

Warning

The mincemeat stays hot after the pastry has cooled down.

Christmas crackers

Place 1 teaspoon of mincemeat on an oblong of pastry about 8 cm by 12 cm (3 in by 5 in).

Brush one long edge with milk to seal it, then roll up the pastry.

With the seam underneath, pinch it into a cracker shape.

Add a small pastry decoration. Glaze and bake, as above.

Use a fish slice to move pastry shapes.

205

Paper cascade

You will need: pencil PVA glue round-ended scissors shiny Christmas wrapping paper patterned Christmas wrapping paper cardboard tube from kitchen paper roll sticky tape ruler fine ribbon kitchen foil

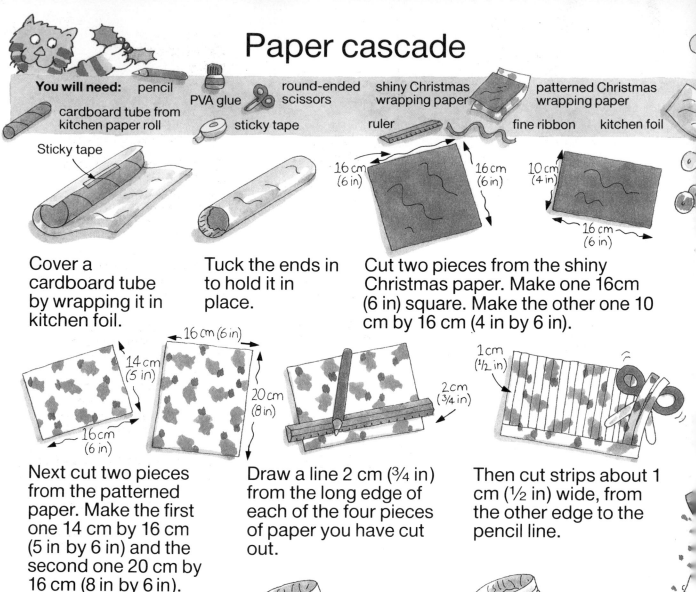

Cover a cardboard tube by wrapping it in kitchen foil.

Tuck the ends in to hold it in place.

Cut two pieces from the shiny Christmas paper. Make one 16cm (6 in) square. Make the other one 10 cm by 16 cm (4 in by 6 in).

Next cut two pieces from the patterned paper. Make the first one 14 cm by 16 cm (5 in by 6 in) and the second one 20 cm by 16 cm (8 in by 6 in).

Draw a line 2 cm (¾ in) from the long edge of each of the four pieces of paper you have cut out.

Then cut strips about 1 cm (½ in) wide, from the other edge to the pencil line.

Take the narrower piece of shiny paper and fix it round the kitchen roll, using sticky tape.

Back of patterned paper.

Stick the narrower, patterned piece on before the other shiny one. The wrong side of the paper should face outwards.

Finish by sticking the widest piece of wrapping paper to the top of the tube.

Fix some ribbon inside at the top with sticky tape.

Cut out shapes from folded shiny paper and stick on the end of some of the strips.

You could add some large sequins or smoothed out sweet papers.

Hang your decoration where it will twist and catch the light.

Turn the cardboard tube upside down and gently pull down the paper strips to show the right side.

Other ideas to try

Fat Stars

Place greaseproof paper over the large star on this page and trace over it.

Fold some coloured paper in half. Put the greaseproof paper on top of it and trace over the lines again to mark the paper below.

Cut out the two star shapes. Lay one star with the wrong side up and cover it with glue.

Stick on a loop of ribbon to make a hanger.

Put a small ball of cotton wool in the centre and flatten it slightly.

Place the second star on top, wrong side down. Press it down to seal the edges.

You could hang three sizes of star on one long ribbon.

Glitter stars

Cut two stars from stiff paper or thin card. Glue each side in turn and sprinkle with glitter.

Leave to dry completely. Cut each star to the centre, as shown.

Slot the stars together and stick a ribbon loop on as a hanger.

Add a bow at the top.

Gingerbread house

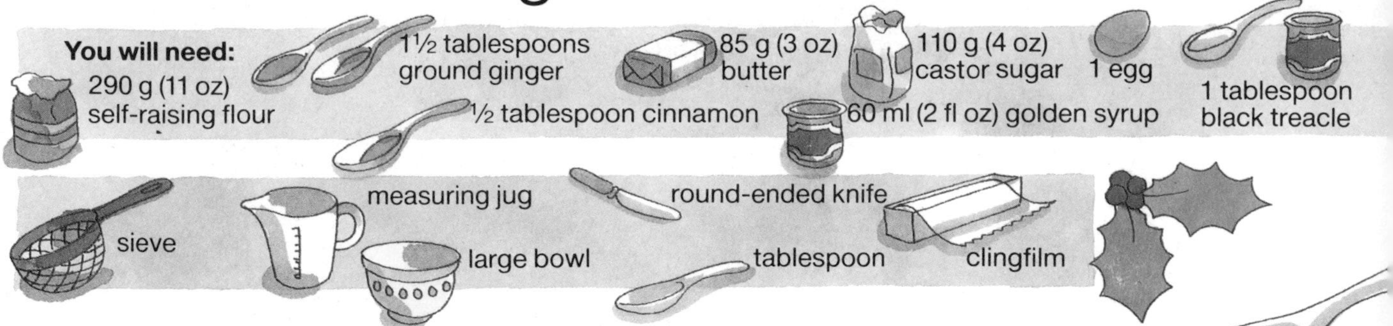

You will need:

290 g (11 oz) self-raising flour

1½ tablespoons ground ginger

85 g (3 oz) butter

110 g (4 oz) castor sugar

1 egg

1 tablespoon black treacle

½ tablespoon cinnamon

60 ml (2 fl oz) golden syrup

sieve

measuring jug

large bowl

round-ended knife

tablespoon

clingfilm

Stage 1: Making the gingerbread dough

Sift the flour and spices into a large bowl. Stir in the castor sugar with a spoon.

Cut the butter into small pieces. Rub it into the flour mixture with your fingers.

Measure the golden syrup into a measuring jug. Add the treacle and an egg. Mix well.

Make a well in the centre of the flour mixture. Add all the liquid at once.

Mix to a dough with a knife.

Wrap the dough in clingfilm and refrigerate it for 30 minutes.

Stage 2: Making the base and roof

You will need: plastic ruler, greaseproof paper, pencil, swiss roll tin, fish-slice, flour, rolling pin

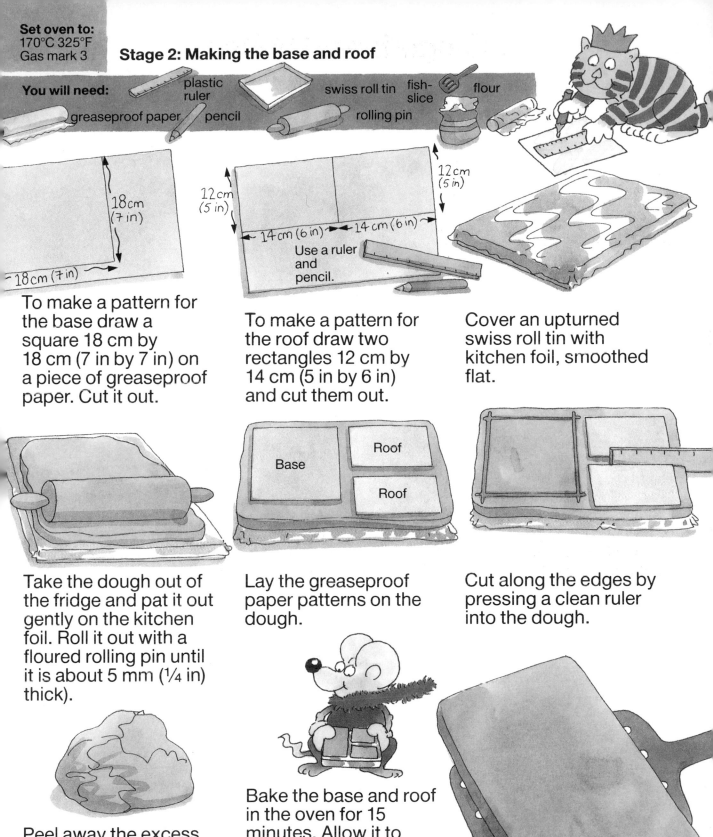

To make a pattern for the base draw a square 18 cm by 18 cm (7 in by 7 in) on a piece of greaseproof paper. Cut it out.

To make a pattern for the roof draw two rectangles 12 cm by 14 cm (5 in by 6 in) and cut them out.

Cover an upturned swiss roll tin with kitchen foil, smoothed flat.

Take the dough out of the fridge and pat it out gently on the kitchen foil. Roll it out with a floured rolling pin until it is about 5 mm (¼ in) thick).

Lay the greaseproof paper patterns on the dough.

Cut along the edges by pressing a clean ruler into the dough.

Peel away the excess dough and keep it wrapped in clingfilm in the refrigerator.

Bake the base and roof in the oven for 15 minutes. Allow it to cool, then ease it off the foil, using a fishslice.

Continued on next page.

Stage 3: Icing and decorating your house

You will need:
225 g (8 oz) icing sugar
egg white powder

bowl

whisk

water

sugar strands

cakeboard
spoon

assortment of different coloured sweets and cake decorations

Mix up some egg white powder with water* and whisk in icing sugar to make a fairly thick paste.

Put the base of the house on a cakeboard. Spread some icing over it and sprinkle it with sugar strands.

Prop the two roof pieces against each other, 3 cm (1 in) from the edge of the base and 1 cm (½ in) from the back.

Put the short sides at the top and bottom.

Hold them together while you dribble icing thickly from a spoon along the top, to seal them together.

Dribble on icing icicles, using a spoon, or pipe it on with an icing bag.

Hints

●If the icing hardens too quickly, dip the sweets in the bowl of icing and glue them on.

●If you haven't got a cakeboard, cover a wooden board or tray and use sticky tape to hold it in position.

Allow the icing to harden a little, then spread more icing over the roof to cover it.

Press sweets or cake decorations into the icing to decorate the roof.

*Follow the instructions on the packet to make the equivalent of one fresh egg white.

Stage 4: Making the witch and the children

You will need:

white marzipan · small gingerbread man cutters · pink, red and blue food colouring · round-ended knife · 3 saucers · rolling pin

Pink ball for head.

White body and arms.

Pink balls for hands.

Red skirt. Press in folds with a knife.

Walking stick.

Colour some marzipan by kneading balls of it in saucers containing a few drops of food colouring.

Roll and cut out the pieces shown above.

Red ball brooch.

Blue shawl.

Press in eyes and a mouth.

Give her a round red nose.

Stand witch in doorway.

Press the pieces together and wrap the shawl round her.

Gingerbread children

Roll out the dough left over when you cut out the base and roof.
Use flour to stop the rolling pin sticking.

Cut out two children with gingerbread man cutters. Use a knife if you don't have cutters.

Bake them in the oven for 15 minutes.

Hold the children in position with icing glue.

211

Nativity scene

You will need: round-ended scissors, coloured tissue paper, clingfilm, a cardboard tube from a toilet roll 10 cm (4 in) high for each figure, plastic tray or wooden board, ruler, large bowl warm water, pencil

Joseph

You could cut several at once.

Cut some tissue paper squares, about 24 cm (9 in) square.

Stand a cardboard tube on a plastic tray or board covered with clingfilm.

Dip a tissue paper square into a bowl of warm water. Lift it out and allow it to drip for a few seconds.

Drape it over the tube and arrange it in folds. Dry in a warm place.

The head

Leave a long tail.

Secure with sticky tape.

Crumple some tissue paper into a ball and wrap it in a tissue paper square. Gather the corners together and twist.

Poke a large hole in the tissue at the top of the tube. Put the base of the head in and fix with tape inside.

Arms

Cut three pieces of tissue about 8 cm by 16 cm (3 in by 6 in).

Crumple two of the pieces and lay them on top of the third piece.

Roll up the third piece, twisting it firmly at both ends.

Pinch the middle flat, then twist two or three times.

sticky tape

felt-tip pens   PVA glue

parcel tape or
ribbon

inside of a large matchbox

drinking
straws

breadknife

Continued on next page.

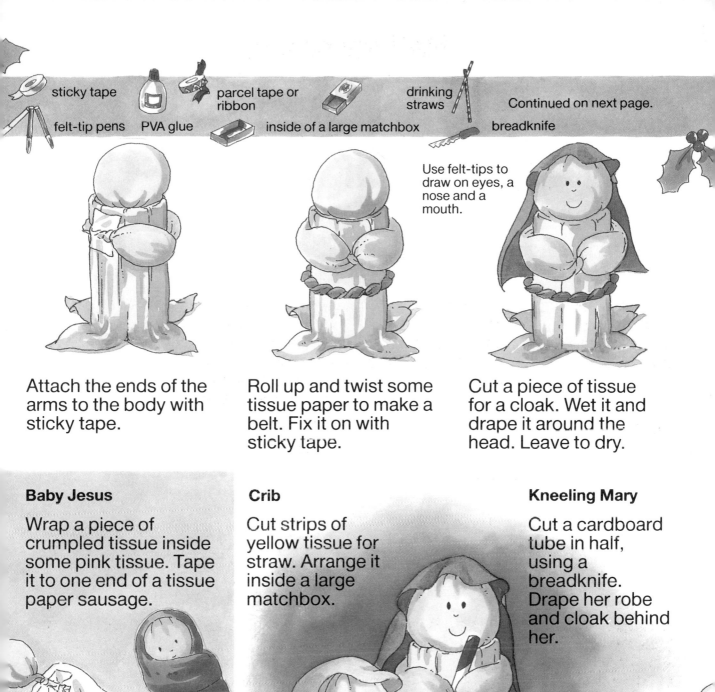

Use felt-tips to
draw on eyes, a
nose and a
mouth.

Attach the ends of the
arms to the body with
sticky tape.

Roll up and twist some
tissue paper to make a
belt. Fix it on with
sticky tape.

Cut a piece of tissue
for a cloak. Wet it and
drape it around the
head. Leave to dry.

Baby Jesus

Wrap a piece of
crumpled tissue inside
some pink tissue. Tape
it to one end of a tissue
paper sausage.

Cut a long strip of
paper, 2 cm (¾ in)
wide. Wrap the baby in
it, starting with the
head. Fix it with sticky
tape. Draw on a face
and place it in the crib.

Crib

Cut strips of
yellow tissue for
straw. Arrange it
inside a large
matchbox.

Kneeling Mary

Cut a cardboard
tube in half,
using a
breadknife.
Drape her robe
and cloak behind
her.

Cut a piece
of straw to
make a
staff.

213

 egg box — 2 bottle tops — feather — cotton wool — kitchen foil — sequins — PVA glue — foil sweet wrapper — painted pasta shell

Shepherds

Use brown, grey and black tissue with plain headbands.

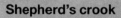

Shepherd's crook

Roll a twisted length of kitchen foil with black or brown tissue. Bend it into shape.

Lambs

Roll cotton wool into sausage shapes for the bodies.
For the heads, wrap crumpled pieces of tissue, inside black tissue rectangles. Twist the corners to make ears. Glue onto the bodies.

The three kings

Headdresses

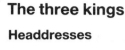

Cut out a section of egg carton. Cover it with kitchen foil.

Trim it with twisted foil and tissue.

Fix sticky tape round base of headdress. Place on head over cloak.

Cover a bottle top with foil. Stick on a small feather or piece of tissue.

Wrap a turban made from twisted tissue paper round the head. Secure it with sticky tape.

Gifts

Painted pasta shell with crumpled foil jewel on top.

Crumpled tissue inside a foil sweet wrapper. Glue on sequins.

Bottle top covered in kitchen foil with gummed paper star stuck on.

Belts

Use shiny parcel ribbon, or twisted kitchen foil.
You could twist kitchen foil and tissue together.

Christmas party games

Christmas puddings

Two or more players

You will need:

- pudding basin
- felt tip pens
- number dice
- 1 sheet of paper for each player
- sultanas
- egg cup

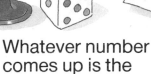

Place the sultanas in the pudding basin and the dice in the egg cup.

Each player draws a large outline of a Christmas pudding on their paper.

The players agree on how many times they will each throw the dice. They then take it in turns to throw it.

Whatever number comes up is the number of sultanas you can take from the pudding bowl and put in your pudding.

The winner is the one with the most sultanas at the end.

Jingle bells

Two or more players

One person goes out of the room and the others choose an object they can see.

The person comes back in and begins to move about the room. The other players chant "Jingle bells" very quietly if they are not near the object, getting louder as they get nearer until the object is found.

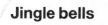

Hint

For "Christmas puddings" instead of a dice you could use six chocolate coins. Stick a gummed star or label on one side of each.

Toss in the air from a small bowl. The number of stars showing when they land is the number of sultanas you can take.

Christmas tree

Any number of players

One player is the questioner. She asks the other players questions.

Whatever the question they must always answer "A Christmas tree". If you giggle when you answer you are out.

Father Christmas

At least three players

One person is the "loader", the others are all Father Christmases.

The loader has a heap of soft toys, boxes and light, unbreakable household objects. She gives each player in turn one item to hold.

The first player to drop something is out.

The last one left in is the real Father Christmas.

Glittery bell card

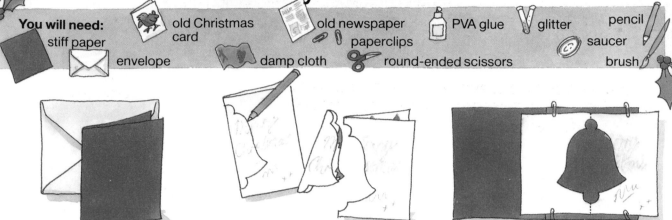

Find an envelope and cut and fold some paper to make a card to fit inside it.

To make a bell stencil draw half a bell shape down the folded edge of an old Christmas card.

Cut the shape out carefully, saving both pieces.

Open out the card you have made. Lay your stencil on the front of it and fix it in position with paperclips.

Working on newspaper, spread glue thinly over the cut-out area of the stencil. Remove the stencil carefully.

Sprinkle glitter over the glued area. Tip the excess off into a saucer to use again.

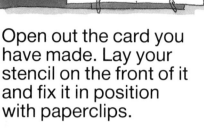

If you use a shiny Christmas card you can wipe your stencil with a damp cloth and use it again.

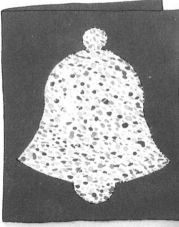

Leave the card to lie flat until the glue is completely dry.

Silhouette card

Use the bell shape cut from the Christmas card above.

Hold it in position in the centre of a card. Dab around the outline with a sponge dipped in white paint, to make a snow effect.

Lift it off carefully. Decorate the bell with sequins, gummed stars, foil scraps or narrow ribbon.

Decorated tree cards

You will need: scraps of coloured paper   doily (white silver or gold)

stick-on gold and silver stars   glitter   narrow parcel ribbon   stiff paper   glue stick

Cut tree shapes from stiff paper and decorate them. Write your message on the back, or stick them onto folded cards.

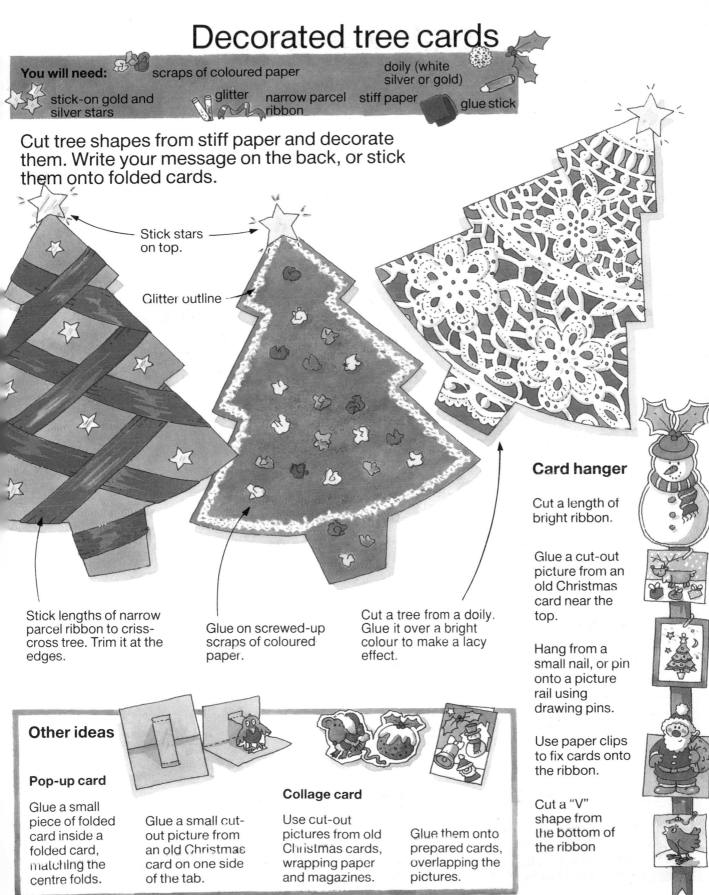

Stick stars on top.

Glitter outline

Stick lengths of narrow parcel ribbon to criss-cross tree. Trim it at the edges.

Glue on screwed-up scraps of coloured paper.

Cut a tree from a doily. Glue it over a bright colour to make a lacy effect.

Card hanger

Cut a length of bright ribbon.

Glue a cut-out picture from an old Christmas card near the top.

Hang from a small nail, or pin onto a picture rail using drawing pins.

Use paper clips to fix cards onto the ribbon.

Cut a "V" shape from the bottom of the ribbon

Other ideas

Pop-up card

Glue a small piece of folded card inside a folded card, matching the centre folds.

Glue a small cut-out picture from an old Christmas card on one side of the tab.

Collage card

Use cut-out pictures from old Christmas cards, wrapping paper and magazines.

Glue them onto prepared cards, overlapping the pictures.

217

Sponge print Christmas card

You will need:
sponge cleaning cloth about 5mm (¼ in) thick

thin cardboard

PVA glue

round coin

thick paintbrush

Christmas tree biscuit cutter (see hints)

strong round-ended scissors

plastic bottle tops

felt-tip pen

Prepare some cards for printing on, by cutting and folding paper to fit in your envelopes.

To make your sponge printing blocks

Cut a piece of cardboard the same size as your sponge cloth.

Working on old newspapers, spread the cardboard with glue and then press the sponge firmly onto it.

Turn the sponge side downwards and draw round your Christmas tree biscuit cutter (see hints) onto the cardboard.

Leave until completely dry, then cut out the tree shape with scissors. Cut it out roughly first, then trim it. Save the leftover pieces.

To make a handle, glue a bottle top to the cardboard side of the tree shape.

Snow printing block

Using leftover pieces of sponge and cardboard snip small shapes.

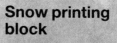

Glue them card side down onto another piece of backing card.

Glue a bottle top handle on the back.

Sun printing block

Draw round a coin, or other round object onto a piece of the leftover card and sponge.

Cut it out and stick on a bottle top handle.

Printing with your shapes

Using a paintbrush, spread green paint evenly over a plate.

Press the tree shape into the paint with the sponge side down. Move it gently from side to side to make sure it is well covered.

Lift off the shape and press onto a card. Press the edges down well, using fingers if necessary. Peel off carefully.

Hints

- If you don't have a Christmas tree biscuit cutter draw a free-hand shape or cut out a cardboard template.

- If you haven't got any bottle tops, you can cut small oblongs from the leftover card and sponge. Glue them on with the card side up.

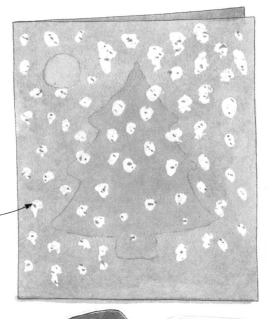

Put yellow paint on a plate and press your round printer into it to print a sun.

Use white paint for your snow print.

You could sprinkle your card with glitter before the paint dries.

Snowman

Cut cardboard shapes for the hat, head and body and scarf.

Add painted eyes, nose and mouth.

Gift tags

Make small cards to print on.

Tie with decorative parcel string or use a hole punch to make a hole in the top left corner. Thread with parcel string.

Nodding reindeer

Reindeer's body

Save the bits you cut off.

Turn the cereal box onto its long side. Cut off the opened end and the bottom panel.

Trim the top panel back 2 cm (¾ in) and round off the corners.

Cut a rectangle 6 cm by 13 cm (2½ in by 5 in) from both sides.

Cut a slit 1 cm by 6 cm (½ in by 2½ in) from the back to form legs.

From the leftover cardboard cut a tail and two ears.

Cut another piece, 4 cm (1½ in) high, and 2 cm (¾ in) wider than the end of the cereal box.

Fold back 1 cm (½ in) each side. This piece will fit between the front legs of the reindeer.

Paint the body and the cut-out pieces brown and leave them to dry.

Reindeer's head

Paint the small box brown. Allow it to dry.

Tape the flap shut if necessary.

Lay the twigs across one end of the box and fix in position with sticky tape to make antlers.

Cut eyes from white paper and glue on. Mark eyes, muzzle and mouth using felt-tip pen.

Stick ears on top of antlers.

Using a ballpoint pen, poke a hole 2 cm (¾ in) from the top edge of the box.

To fix the head and body together

Leave the ends at least 5 cm (2 in) long.

Leave about 2 cm (¾ in) between the pencil and the tape.

Tie a thread round a pencil. You should be able to slide the loop up and down the pencil.

Suspend the pencil by taping the threads to the inside top centre of the body.

Poke the pencil into the hole in the back of the head.

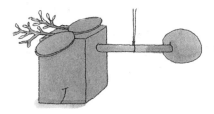

Press a ball of playdough onto the other end of the pencil, so that the head swings up a little.

If the head is too low add more playdough, if too high take a little off.

Slide the pencil through the loop if necessary, to adjust the angle of the head. The reindeer should nod freely when you tap his head.

Glue the tail onto the back.

The front panel goes between the front legs.

Finishing off

Put glue on the end of the tail and stick it onto the body.

Glue the sides of the front panel and stick it between the front legs to strengthen them.

Chocolate money tree

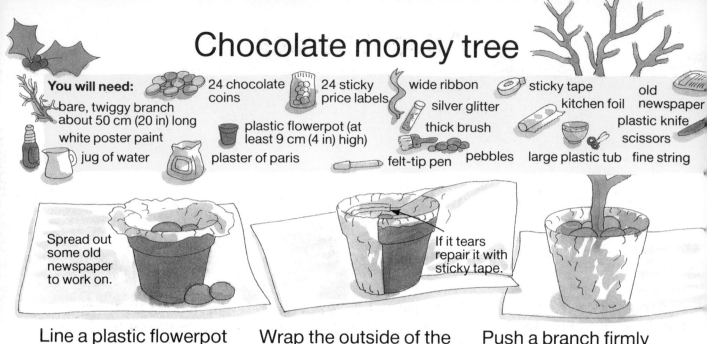

You will need:
bare, twiggy branch about 50 cm (20 in) long
white poster paint
jug of water
24 chocolate coins
plastic flowerpot (at least 9 cm (4 in) high)
plaster of paris
24 sticky price labels
wide ribbon
silver glitter
thick brush
felt-tip pen
pebbles
sticky tape
kitchen foil
old newspaper
plastic knife
scissors
large plastic tub
fine string

Spread out some old newspaper to work on.

If it tears repair it with sticky tape.

Line a plastic flowerpot with tinfoil to make it water tight. Put some pebbles at the bottom.

Wrap the outside of the pot in tinfoil. Tuck it under the base and over the rim.

Push a branch firmly into the pot between the pebbles until it touches the bottom.

Use a plastic knife.

In a plastic tub mix up some plaster of paris* with water until it is smooth and creamy.

Pour the plaster of paris round the branch, over the pebbles. Hold the branch upright until the plaster sets.
  Paint the branches white. Sprinkle them with glitter as you go, before the paint dries.

Hang the coins from the branch.

Tie a large ribbon around the pot in a bow. Tape it at the sides to prevent it slipping.

14

Cut some string into pieces about 15 cm (6 in) long. Tape the ends of each piece to a coin to make a loop.

Number some sticky labels from one to 24. Peel them off and stick them onto the coins.

Snip off one coin each day from December 1 until Christmas Eve. You could replace the coins with small ornaments, ribbon bows or pictures cut from old Christmas cards.

*For advice on using plaster of paris see page 200.

Advent parcel

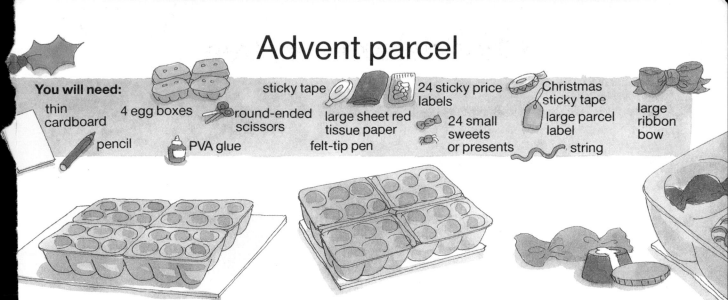

You will need:
thin cardboard · 4 egg boxes · sticky tape · round-ended scissors · large sheet red tissue paper · 24 sticky price labels · 24 small sweets or presents · Christmas sticky tape · large parcel label · large ribbon bow · pencil · PVA glue · felt-tip pen · string

Cut the tops off four egg boxes. Glue the underside of the bottom halves and place them on a sheet of thin cardboard.

Trim the card around the edges. Tape across the joins between the boxes.

Fill each section with a small sweet or toy (see below for ideas).

Brush glue along the tops of the egg boxes. Lay the tissue paper across them and press gently to the glued areas.

Tuck the overlapping tissue underneath. Turn the boxes over carefully and tape the tissue down.

Add a ribbon bow and a label.

Stick Christmas tape over the tissue paper, where the boxes join.

Hint
- If you have not got any sticky labels cut up some gummed paper squares.

To hang it up, knot both ends of a piece of string and tape it to the back of the parcel.

Number some sticky labels from one to 24 and stick one over each compartment in a random order.

From December 1 open one section each day by poking the tissue with a pencil.

Ideas for filling parcel: sweets · plastic ring or necklace · plastic spider · hairslide · soap shape · balloons · small rubber ball · chocolate coin · badge · paper hat · small coin · toy watch

223

Parents' notes

Gather together everything you will need for a project before you start, checking off each item with your child from the panels at the top of the pages.

Below are a few notes about some of the materials and equipment you will need.

Scissors

When working with young children it is always best to use round-ended scissors for safety. If you use sharp scissors at all, put them out of reach immediately after you have used them.

Glue

PVA (polyvinyl acetate) is the best glue to use for most of the projects. It is white, but dries transparent. Protect clothing with aprons and wash brushes out carefully after use. Don't use solvent-based glues.

Paints

Poster paint has good covering power. When covering large areas use small adult decorating brushes.

Breadknife

This is the best thing to use to cut through cardboard tubes, boxes etc. Use a sawing action and protect work surfaces with a thick layer of old newspaper.

Sticky tape

When you need to use several pieces cut them all at once and attach them lightly to the edge of your work surface for easy use.

Patterned or shiny Christmas tape is useful for decorating things.

Mixing containers

Use plastic icecream or margarine tubs for mixing plaster or watering down paint.

Glitter

When using glitter sprinkle it directly from the tube. Tip off the excess onto a piece of paper which has been folded in half then opened out. Refold the paper and pour the excess glitter back into the tube.

Plaster of paris

This can be bought from large chemists' shops.

Mix it slowly in a large tub so that the powder does not puff out.

To get rid of excess plaster, pour it into a plastic bag and wait for it to set before putting it in the bin.

Decorations

Bits of gold or glittery braid

Non-flammable tinsel

White, gold or silver doilies

Sequins

Beads

Coloured string

Scraps of felt

Cotton wool

Make sure that any tree decorations you buy for trimming are nonbreakable.

Paper and cardboard

The following types will come in handy: Christmas wrapping paper – new or used

Foil-backed paper – avoid the plastic kind, it's hard to handle.

Old Christmas cards

Kitchen foil – covers large areas well

Crêpe paper

Sweet wrappers – foil and cellophane

Cereal cardboard

Greaseproof paper – for tracing

Tissue paper

Ribbon

Florists' ribbon is inexpensive and curls well.